Sanitation without Water

Supplied by:
TALC
P.O. Box 49
St. Albans
Herts AL1 5TX U.K.

Related titles published by Macmillan

Peter Morgan: *Rural Water Supply and Sanitation*   ISBN 0 – 333 – 48569 – 6
T K Lankester: *Setting up Community Health Programmes*   ISBN 0 – 333 – 57423 – 0
M T Feuerstein: *Partners in Evaluation*   ISBN 0 – 333 – 42261 – 9
David Werner: *Where there is No Doctor*   ISBN 0 – 333 – 51651 – 6
R Amonoo-Lartson, G J Ebrahim, H J Lovell and
  J P Ranken: *District Health Care*   ISBN 0 – 333 – 36601 – 8
  (ELBS edition)   ISBN 0 – 333 – 39762 – 2

The paperback edition of this book is available at a reduced price. This has been made possible by a generous subsidy provided by the Swedish International Development Authority (SIDA). The publishers and the authors would like to acknowledge the valuable role of SIDA in this respect.

Sanitation without Water

Uno Winblad
and
Wen Kilama

Illustrations by Kjell Torstensson

Revised and Enlarged Edition

MACMILLAN

Published with the support of the Swedish International
Development Authority

The first edition of this book was published by the authors
with the support of SIDA, the Swedish International
Development Authority, Stockholm

This revised and enlarged edition first published 1985 by
MACMILLAN EDUCATION LTD
London and Oxford
Companies and representatives throughout the world

ISBN 0–333–39140–3

20   19   18   17   16   15   14   13   12   11
09   08   07   06   05   04   03   02   01   00

This book is printed on paper suitable for recycling and
made from fully managed and sustained forest sources.

Printed in China

CONTENTS

PREFACE

This edition has been extensively revised and rewritten since it first appeared in 1978. We have added several new examples and many illustrations. The most significant change, however, is that we have now included simple pour-flush latrines. We have done this because a pour-flush latrine is often an alternative to the drop latrines described in the earlier edition. A new chapter 4 deals with the selection of the right type of latrine. We have also added an appendix on how to build a soakpit for the disposal of waste water.

Sweden and Tanzania, 1984   U.W.
                                                                                W.K.

ACKNOWLEDGEMENTS

The publication of this monograph was made possible by a grant from SIDA, the Swedish International Development Authority, Stockholm.

The research and development behind this book have been supported by a number of institutions over several years. The Scandinavian Institute of African Studies, Uppsala, provided a travel grant in 1970; DANIDA, the Danish International Development Agency, Copenhagen, awarded a research grant in 1971; IDRC, the International Development Research Centre, Ottawa, funded a comparative study of compost latrines in Tanzania in 1974 - 78, and a study tour to China in 1975; the Swedish Institute, Stockholm, contributed a travel grant in 1974; the Tanzania National Scientific Research Council in cooperation with the Faculty of Medicine, University of Dar-es-Salaam, provided personnel, accommodation and laboratory facilities for field experiments and laboratory tests in 1975 - 78; SIDA provided a travel grant in 1980; and the Ethiopian Science and Technology Commission financed a seminar in Ethiopia in 1980. The current revision has been funded by SIDA via TALC, Teaching Aids at Low Cost, London, in 1983.

To all institutions and to friends and colleagues who critically examined the previous edition we wish to express our sincere appreciation. Our grateful thanks go also to Pauline Robinson for her help with the organization and text of the book.

The views expressed in this book are those of the authors and do not necessarily represent those of the personnel within the institutions sponsoring the research, development and publication.

1 INTRODUCTION

The Western type of toilet system cannot solve the problems of getting rid of excreta in Third World countries. Nor, indeed, has it solved those problems in the developed world.

The Western system is expensive. It uses large amounts of clean water to flush away a small amount of excreta. It dirties streams, lakes and groundwater. For the large majority of people who still have no piped water, such a system is not even something to consider.

1.1 Situation

Let us consider a basic fact of life: all people, old and young, rich and poor, need to get rid of waste matter every day. The technical term for these wastes is *excreta*. Excreta consist of *faeces* (solid matter) and *urine* (liquid matter).

A basic distinction between people is that some are 'washers' and some are 'wipers'. These words refer to how people clean themselves after they have excreted. Washers use water, wipers use some solid material like grass, leaves, paper, sticks, corncobs, mudballs or stones.

Every culture has developed methods of dealing with excreta. In chapter 3 of this book we describe, sometimes for the first time, many such methods.

In all cultures there are taboos surrounding defecation practices. For example, people who empty buckets and clean latrines may be regarded as outcasts. Men and women, or adults and children, may not be allowed to use the same latrine. Your enemy, if he gets hold of your faeces, can cause you great harm. Evil spirits may live in the pit.

Religion may lay down strict rules for the position and use of latrines. Religion may even lay down rules for cleaning after defecation.

1.2   Problems

Unfortunately, there are many problems connected with traditional defecation practices. The most serious ones are health problems. Human faeces can contain harmful organisms. Many diseases can spread because people have come into contact with faeces.

Practices like defecating in the bush, in fields, or in open pits may be all right in sparsely populated areas. Such practices are dangerous, however, in areas where people do live close together, for example compact villages or urban areas. When people move from the country-side to villages and towns, they need to develop new practices that are more suitable for those areas. This is particularly important today, when populations are increasing and so many people are moving.

Traditional practices have other disadvantages. One example is in India. Here the village women must walk out into the fields in the early morning in order to defecate away from the sight of men. The women are often afraid of being raped or attacked by snakes, tigers and other wild animals.

Another problem is that faeces and urine have an unpleasant smell. Fresh faeces attract flies and other insects. People need methods that help them to get rid of bad smells, filth flies, etc.

Excreta disposal can be expensive, especially where many people live close together. In large cities in developing countries, only the rich have a satisfactory disposal system. Most people have to manage with self-built, smelly and insanitary latrines.

1.3   Solutions

To solve the problems we have to consider not only technical but also environmental and human factors.

There is no 'best' technical solution for all situations all over the world. Technical solutions must be adapted to the local environment, the financial resources, the skills and the traditional 'latrine behaviour' of the user. People need to choose the latrine that is best for their area and for their traditional culture. For example, a pour-flush latrine works well for a family which uses water for anal cleaning but will not work at all for people using solid materials like sticks or stones.

When choosing a latrine, we must consider such things as: are

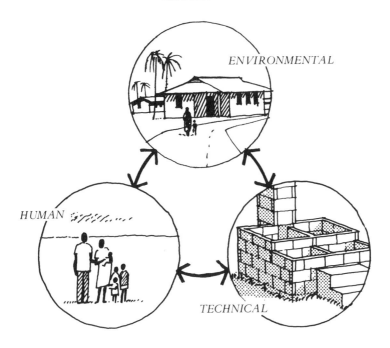

Figure 1 The success or failure of a latrine system depends on the interaction
of three sets of factors: environmental, human and technical

people washers or wipers, what is the climate like, what type of soil
is there, where is the groundwater, and what materials and skills are
locally available?

1.4 About this book

In this book we aim to give practical information on a range of possible technical solutions. The emphasis is on simple measures that
people can carry out with limited funds, equipment and materials.
We concentrate on sanitation systems for individual households. Public
latrines for markets, railway stations, schools and hospitals are only
mentioned briefly here. Most of the latrine systems we describe in
the following chapters can be used in public buildings and institutions.
The problem there is not so much design and construction of the
latrine, but rather supervision, cleaning and maintenance.

We are not dealing with complex and expensive systems like septic tanks and biogas plants. They are well covered by other handbooks. Nor have we gone into health education. That important subject deserves its own book.

Our aim has been to produce a simple, readable and well illustrated manual for health officers, nurses, medical auxiliaries, village health workers and community workers. It should also be of relevance to medical officers interested in disease prevention, and to planners, architects and civil and sanitary engineers concerned with appropriate technology.

2 SANITATION AND DISEASE

Many infections of human beings are spread through inadequate sanitation. Viruses, bacteria. protozoa and worms may spread through direct contact, indirectly via food, water and soil. or via carriers and vectors.

In this chapter we shall look at the common methods by which diseases spread. We shall mention the most important diseases connected with poor sanitation, and we shall outline preventive measures. We shall not discuss symptoms and treatment, as information of that kind is readily available in medical textbooks.

2.1 Infection from taking in food or drink contaminated with faeces

Viral diseases like poliomyelitis, infectious hepatitis and gastroenteritis; bacterial diseases like cholera, typhoid, paratyphoid and bacillary dysentery; protozoal diseases like amoebic dysentery and giardiasis; and worm infections like ascariasis, trichuriasis and pinworm are passed on when people touch faeces and then food or drink.

Today we control polio by vaccinating infants and children. For all the other diseases mentioned above, the most important measure is to dispose of faeces in a sanitary way, and to protect food and water supplies. It is important to control filth flies (we discuss a variety of methods in appendix 2 to this book). It is also essential to protect food from flies and cockroaches. Health education, stressing personal hygiene and the sanitary handling of food and drinking water, is also very important.

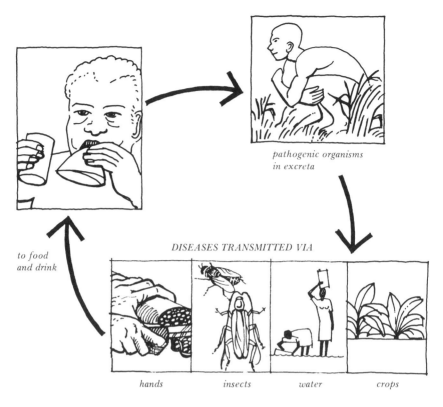

pathogenic organisms
in excreta

to food
and drink

DISEASES TRANSMITTED VIA

hands   insects   water   crops

Figure 2   The faecal–oral route: infections are spread or transmitted from the faeces of one person to his or another person's mouth by contaminated food and drink or directly by dirty hands

2.2   Infection from eating beef or pork infected with tapeworm

The most important tapeworms in human beings are passed on via cattle and pigs. Infected people pass worm segments in their faeces. When the segments break up, they release eggs. Cattle or pigs grazing on infested ground eat the eggs, which then develop in their muscles. Human beings get the infection by eating raw or undercooked infected meat. Under suitable conditions, eggs can stay viable in pastures for eight or more weeks.

In order to prevent tapeworm infections, people must dispose of their faeces in a sanitary way, so that cattle and pigs cannot come into contact with them. Health education programmes must emphasize

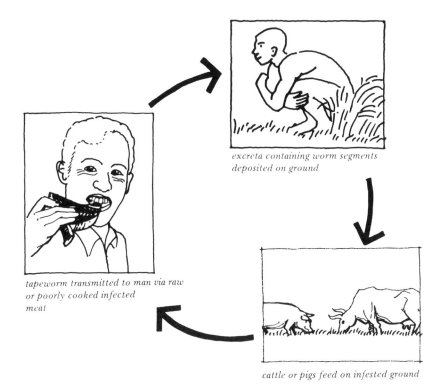

excreta containing worm segments deposited on ground

tapeworm transmitted to man via raw or poorly cooked infected meat

cattle or pigs feed on infested ground

Figure 3   How tapeworms are spread

that it is dangerous to pollute soil or water with human excreta. People must always cook all their meat thoroughly.

2.3   Infection from contact with water

A major disease passed on via infected water is schistosomiasis (bilharziasis). It is caused by blood flukes, causing either urinary schistosomiasis or intestinal schistosomiasis.

Human beings pollute water with infected urine or faeces containing schistosome eggs. People get the infection while bathing, swimming, washing, fishing, cultivating or collecting plants in the polluted waters as schistosome larvae in the water penetrate the skin.

It is difficult to control schistosomiasis and the disease is increasing in many parts of the developing world. Effective drugs are expensive,

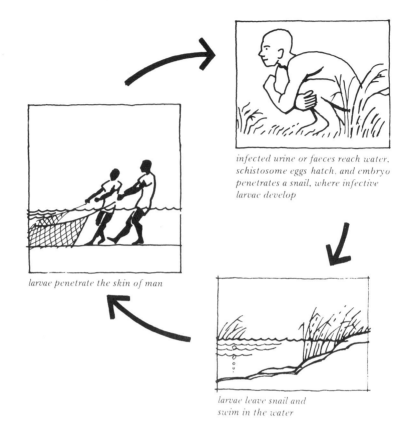

infected urine or faeces reach water, schistosome eggs hatch, and embryo penetrates a snail, where infective larvae develop

larvae penetrate the skin of man

larvae leave snail and swim in the water

Figure 4   How schistosome worms are spread

while less expensive drugs have bad side effects. Most people cannot avoid becoming reinfected soon after treatment anyway. The chemicals used to control the snail vector are also expensive, pollute the water and give only temporary control. If people had an adequate and safe water supply, then this would reduce their exposure to infected water. This would, however, have little effect when people fish, work in irrigated fields, or collect water plants.

An essential measure against schistosomiasis is to dispose of human excreta in a sanitary way. This means that people must use latrines. Because it is difficult to control schistosomiasis, we must try to combine a number of measures, and emphasize sanitation in particular.

2.4   Infection from contact with soil

Certain parasitic worms such as hookworms penetrate the skin from damp soil polluted with faeces. Infected human beings pass faeces which contain hookworm eggs. The eggs hatch into larvae, which feed on organic waste and bacteria. Under optimal conditions they develop into infective larvae in about one week and remain viable for up to five weeks.

Many drugs are available for the treatment of hookworm infection. However, even when people have been treated, they are often infected again when they return home. Hookworm control can only come from a combination of sanitation with mass treatment and health education programmes.

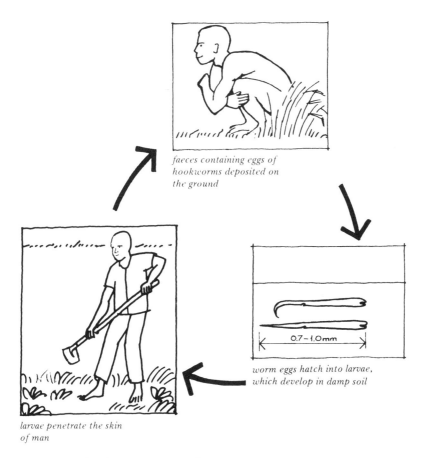

faeces containing eggs of hookworms deposited on the ground

worm eggs hatch into larvae, which develop in damp soil

0.7 – 1.0 mm

larvae penetrate the skin of man

Figure 5   How hookworms are spread

2.5   Infection via insect vectors

Bancroftian filariasis is a serious disease which is indirectly related to the disposal of excreta. The end result of this disease is elephantiasis, mainly affecting the legs and, in males, the genital organs. Bancroftian filariasis is caused by a parasite. It is passed on by means of a suitable mosquito species, which in the urbanized tropical and subtropical world is the *Culex* mosquito.

This mosquito breeds in foul water: drains, cesspits, faulty septic tanks, aqua privies, pit latrines and any other water with a high content of organic matter. The rapid growth of unplanned and poorly serviced urban areas in Africa, Asia and Latin America has led to tremendous increases in *Culex* mosquito populations.

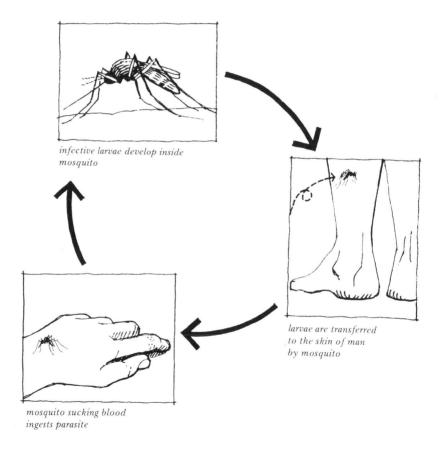

infective larvae develop inside mosquito

larvae are transferred to the skin of man by mosquito

mosquito sucking blood ingests parasite

Figure 6   How Bancroftian filariasis is spread

The installation of latrines may in fact result in an increase of mosquitoes. In East Africa. villages with latrines are more likely to have *Culex* mosquitoes than villages without latrines. As a consequence, there is an increase of Bancroftian filariasis.

Culex mosquitoes can be controlled with insecticides, but it is a method with many limitations. The cost is extremely high. Mosquitoes often develop resistance. Insecticides are toxic to human beings and to animals. The risk of water pollution is high as the insecticides have to be applied often – in many cases every week.

People can protect themselves with mosquito repellents, bed nets, screened houses and protective clothing. At the community level, the most important preventive measure is to avoid creating breeding habitats. Latrines should preferably be dry and should therefore not reach down into the groundwater. Aqua privies, septic tanks and pour-flush latrines must be perfectly sealed.

2.6   Conclusions

There are no short-cuts to improved public health in developing countries. Vaccination, chemotherapy and insecticides are in most cases of limited value. Lasting results can only be achieved with the general introduction of satisfactory systems for water supply, waste-water disposal and sanitation together with intensive health education programmes.

3 EXAMPLES OF SANITATION WITHOUT WATER

3.1 Introduction

In this chapter we present and comment on a number of systems of excreta disposal from various parts of the world. The selection represents a wide variety of cultural, environmental and economic conditions.

In terms of culture, there are two approaches to excreta disposal:

- Some people regard human excreta as a valuable resource. This approach should lead to a *composting system*.

- Some people regard human excreta as an unpleasant and dangerous waste product. They dispose of their excreta and do not make any further use of it. The resulting system may be called a *final disposal system*.

We have included systems that are suitable for areas where the groundwater table is low and systems that can be used under any groundwater conditions. We include examples from areas where the houses are close together and from areas where the houses are not so close together. We include examples from rich countries and from poor countries. Some systems may function only where water is used for anal cleaning but most will work with any cleaning material.

3.2 China

The Chinese have made compost from human and animal excreta for thousands of years. In 1952 an estimated 70% of all human excreta produced in China was collected and used as fertilizer. In 1956 this

Figure 7   A latrine combined with pig-pen

figure had increased to 90%, altogether some 300 million tons (Dorozynski 1975). At the time that represented one-third of all fertilizers used in the country.

In rural areas people often combined the latrine with a pig-pen in such a way that the pigs could feed on human excreta. The Chinese do not do this any longer. The authorities decided it was not hygienic, and besides some of the fertilizer value of the human excreta is lost. Existing combined latrine/pig-pen units are rebuilt and the latrine separated from the pen and turned into a 'shallow pit'. This pit is no more than 0.10–0.15 metre deep. By a 'deep pit' the Chinese generally mean one that is 0.40–0.50 metre deep. The Chinese prefer shallow pits because they are easier to empty and keep clean.

The shallow pit is normally designed for separation of faeces and urine. The urine is collected in a pan, placed directly in front of the

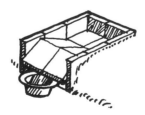

Figure 8   A Chinese shallow latrine with separation of faeces and urine

latrine as in figure 8, or drained away through a channel to a urine pit or a jar at some distance away from the latrine. The pit is emptied daily and its contents brought to a compost station where they are mixed with animal manure, refuse and soil.

Bucket latrines are still common in China. The buckets are often made of wood and beautifully laquered. People take the contents of

Figure 9   Wooden latrine buckets with lids

buckets and shallow pits to the compost station. The excreta are carried in willow baskets, pails or other containers or transported on special tricycles. These methods are used not only in villages, but also in large cities.

Figure 10   A tricycle for transport of excreta

During a study visit to Canton in 1975 we were told that the collection of excreta in that city used to be controlled by unscrupulous racketeers who sold the excreta to peasants. These practices were stopped after the liberation and a special organization was set up to collect, treat and distribute all household residues. After the collectivization movement in 1956, peasants started coming into Canton to do their own collection. As many as 15 000 commune members would enter the city every night, empty the latrines and buckets and carry the treasure back to the villages. Leaking containers and careless handling caused spilling and unsanitary conditions. The collection has now been reorganized and is carried out by salaried sanitary workers. In 1975 the communes around Canton paid from Yuan 3.40 to 5.58 per ton for nightsoil — the exact price depending on water content. (Normal wages at the time were Yuan 60–70 per month.)

At the compost station, the excreta are treated. The purpose of the treatment is to destroy pathogens without losing any fertilizer value. There are various methods: these range from anaerobic fermentation in tanks to aerobic composting in heaps or pits.

A common method is 'four into one' composting under high temperature (McGarry and Stainforth 1978). This method uses four types of raw material: human excreta, animal manure, soil and street sweepings.

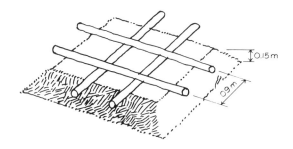

Figure 11 A ventilated compost pile under construction. Dimensions are in metres

When the Chinese make a high-temperature compost, this is how they do it. First they mix roughly equal proportions of the raw materials. They pile the mixture 0.15 metre high. If the mixture is too dry, they add water. On top of the pile they place four pieces of timber of 70–100 millimetres diameter (or a bundle of millet stalks) as shown here. The distance between timbers is about 0.9 metre.

At the crossing points the compost makers put four vertical pieces of the same dimensions (see figure 12). They pile up raw material to

Figure 12   Wooden poles are used to form horizontal and vertical channels
            through the compost pile

a total height of 0.9 metre. Finally they cover the pile with a 50 millimetres thick soil/manure mix (two-thirds soil, one-third manure).
The earth covering serves several purposes: it prevents rainwater
from soaking the pile, reduces evaporation, lessens loss of nitrogen,
checks fly breeding and odours, and increases the surface temperature.

When the covering mix is dry, they pull out the timber pieces. Air
movement through the holes keeps the decomposition process aerobic.

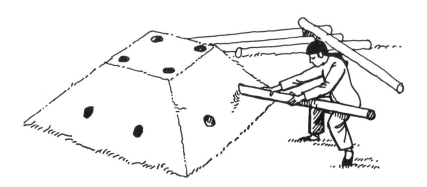

Figure 13   The compost pile completed

In spring and autumn, the compost operator blocks the holes at night to prevent cooling. In summer, when compost temperatures reach 50°C, he blocks the holes to check evaporation rate and nitrogen loss. In winter, the piles are often built without holes.

In winter the humidity of the compost is kept at around 30%, in late spring and early summer it should be around 40%, and in summer it is raised to about 50%. A skilled compost operator is able to estimate the humidity from poking the pile with a stick.

Compost temperatures usually increase to 50–60°C. After 20 days in summer and up to 60 days in winter the crude compost has matured and is ready for application on the fields.

The urine that was collected separately can be added to the compost but more commonly it is diluted with water (one part urine to five parts water) and used directly on vegetable plots.

The Chinese method of high-temperature composting does not pollute streams or lakes. There is no harm to groundwater or soil. Humus and nutrients removed by intensive cultivation are returned to the soil.

From a health point of view it is doubtful though. Buckets and shallow pits are emptied and cleaned daily and their contents are transported. This means a lot of handling of fresh excreta, risk of spilling, and many opportunities for flies to come into contact with faeces. However, the Chinese have a long experience of handling excreta and the general standard of hygiene is such that they are nowadays able to cope with the health hazards.

The running costs of this system are high but the Chinese put an even higher value on the excreta.

3.3   Vietnam

In parts of Vietnam, as in China, it was common practice to fertilize rice fields with fresh excreta. In other parts of the country 'People were in the habit of relieving themselves in the fields or at the sides of the less frequented roads, leaving their excreta for sustenance for the famished dogs' (McMichael 1976).

In 1956 the health authorities of the Democratic Republic of Vietnam started campaigns to construct latrines. After many experi-

.nents the peasants of the Quang Ngai Province developed 'the double septic tank for on-the-spot composting of excreta'. (To avoid confusion we shall not use the term 'septic tank' for this dry double-vault latrine.)

In its first five-year plan (1961–65) the Ministry of Health concentrated on what it called 'the three major installations for rural hygiene', namely the double-vault latrine, the lined well and the bathroom.

The Vietnamese latrine consists of a receptacle divided into two vaults, each with a volume of about 300 litres. The Vietnamese build

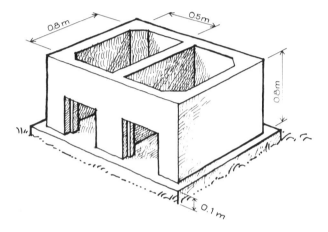

Figure 14   The receptacle of a Vietnamese compost latrine. The receptacle is divided into two vaults. Dimensions are in metres

the latrine entirely above ground with the receptacle placed on a solid floor of concrete, bricks or clay. They build up the floor to at least 0.1 metre above ground so that heavy rains do not flood it. They place the latrine at least 10 metres away from dwelling houses and water tanks.

The receptacle is covered with a squatting slab which has two holes, footrests and a channel for urine. Both holes have tight-fitting lids (not shown on the figures). In front there are steps leading up to the squatting slab. At the back there are two openings, 0.3 × 0.3 metre, for the removal of the mature compost. These openings are kept sealed until it is time to empty one of the vaults.

People excrete in one of the vaults. Before the vault is used for the first time, the household members cover the bottom with a layer of powdered earth. The purpose of this earth is to absorb moisture from

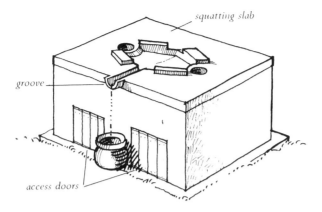

Figure 15   The Vietnamese compost latrine seen from the back. The squatting
slab has a pan for separation of urine

the faeces, to prevent the faeces from sticking to the floor, and also
to provide some of the micro-organisms for the process of decomposition. After each use people sprinkle two bowls of ashes over the
faeces. The ashes absorb moisture, neutralize bad odours and make
the faeces less attractive to flies.

Urine drains away through the groove in the slab and collects in a
jar behind the latrine. Thus in the receptacle there are only faeces,
ashes, soil and toilet paper. The contents are therefore fairly dry and
compact. The process of decomposition is, according to Vietnamese
sources (Democratic Republic of Vietnam, Ministry of Health 1968),
basically anaerobic.

The jar for urine can be empty or partly filled with water, lime or
ashes.

The first vault can be used for about two months by a household
of 5–10 persons. When it is two-thirds full, someone in the household levels the contents with a stick. He or she then fills the vault to
the brim with dried, powdered earth, and seals the vault. All openings
are tightly closed with lime mortar or clay. The other vault now
comes into use instead. When after another two months the second
vault is nearly full, he or she opens and empties the first vault.

The temperature inside the vault is normally 2–6°C higher than
outside. In summer, while the outside temperature is 28–32°C, the
temperature inside a closed vault may come close to 50°C.

Around the latrine the Vietnamese grow insect-repellent plants
like citronella.

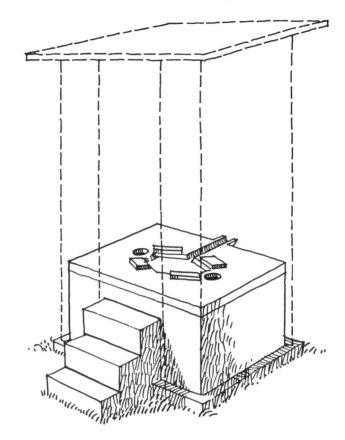

Figure 16   The Vietnamese compost latrine seen from the front. In areas that
are seasonally flooded the latrine is built entirely above ground and
has steps leading up to the squatting slab

The Vietnamese health authorities claim that after 45 days in a
sealed receptacle 'all bacteria and pathogenic viruses, all eggs and
embryos of intestinal parasites are killed, and toxic organic matters
mineralized ' (McMichael 1976).

The decomposed faeces, now odourless, make an excellent fertilizer.
Experiments in agricultural cooperatives in Vietnam show that compost from double-vault latrines increases the yield of crops by 10–25%
in comparison with fresh excreta (Democratic Republic of Vietnam,
Ministry of Health 1968).

People in rural areas all over Vietnam now use this system. In her
book *Health in the Third World*, Dr Joan McMichael (1976) states
that of all the public health measures put into operation by the

Vietnamese, the double-vault latrine has perhaps been the single most important factor in the prevention of disease and the promotion of health:

'It strikes at the root cause of many of the most intractible diseases of the developing countries – the gastro-intestinal infections, cholera, dysentery and the typhoids – and checks the menace of fly borne infections. Last but perhaps no less important, it solves, in part at least, the problems of fertilizing the soil, since the yearly amount of sterilized organic manure that can thus be obtained is estimated at 600 000 tons.'

Long and persistent health education programmes were necessary in order to obtain these achievements. The task was not easy. Some people found the latrine too expensive and complicated. In the north the peasants believed that manuring with fresh faeces was better than with composted faeces. In certain villages people did not use the latrines in the correct way, which caused odours and heavy fly breeding. In some cases both vaults were used, one by men and the other by women (Democratic Republic of Vietnam, Ministry of Health 1968).

The Vietnamese system of composting excreta does not pollute streams, ponds, groundwater or soil. When the excreta are finally returned to the soil, they have already been transformed into humus through the decomposition taking place in the receptacle.

Most compost latrine systems need a lot of kitchen and garden refuse to get a favourable carbon/nitrogen ratio (see chapter 9). The Vietnamese add only ashes, toilet paper and soil and make sure no urine enters the vault. It is because the Vietnamese take care of the urine separately that they do not have to add refuse.

From a health point of view this system is good as long as the urine does not reach fresh water. Nobody touches the faeces. There is not much fly breeding if everyone sprinkles ashes over his faeces.

The Vietnamese keep the faeces in the closed vault for only two months. Is this really enough? The longer the faeces are stored, the less is the risk that the pathogenic organisms will survive.

As the Vietnamese build the receptacle entirely above ground, and do not let any water or urine into the vaults, the contents are dry. *Culex* mosquitoes therefore cannot breed in this type of latrine.

The construction is simple and the Vietnamese farmers can build the latrine entirely from locally available materials. (The Vietnamese sources do not mention the fact that urine can wear away concrete. This might be a problem.)

3.4   Guatemala

A variation of the Vietnamese latrine was introduced by the Centro Mesoamericano de Estudios sobre Tecnologia Apropriada (CEMAT) in the Lake Atitlán area of Guatemala in 1978 (van Buren *et al*. 1984). Because of volcanic bedrock and lack of space, the Guatemalans could not use ordinary pit latrines. For this reason, and also because they wanted to turn excreta into fertilizer, CEMAT in consultation with the local population chose the Vietnamese type.

The Guatemalans build their latrines above ground, using local materials. They use compacted soil, adobe, bricks, concrete, lime-pozzolana or stone blocks for the walls of the receptacle. They use concrete or bamboo and cane for the platform. On the top there is a movable seat with a urine collector from which the urine flows via a pipe into a container. After dilution with water it is used as a fertilizer. Alternatively the urine may flow from the collector directly into a soakpit. The raised seat has a lid. At the back of the vaults there are openings for the removal of compost. There is no ventpipe from the receptacle.

Each time they defecate, people then sprinkle ashes or a soil/lime mixture on the faeces. The receptacle thus receives only faeces, ashes or soil/lime and whatever is used for anal cleaning. Every week the contents of the receptacle are stirred with a stick and more ashes added. When the first vault is nearly full the seat is placed above the second vault. The first vault is topped up with earth and the opening in the platform closed. Two or three months later, when the second vault is nearly full, the first one is opened and emptied. The raised seat is now returned to its first position.

In Guatemala the cost of this type of latrine ranges from the equivalent of US $35 for adobe to US $70 for concrete block construction.

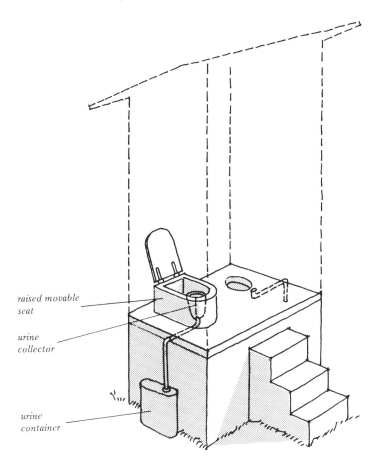

raised movable
seat

urine
collector

urine
container

Figure 17   A double-vault compost latrine with separation of urine, tried in
            Guatemala

Extension workers (here called promoters) introduce the new
latrine. They arrange slide shows and visits by villagers to places
where latrines have already been built. In villages where there is
enough interest, they arrange courses of instruction. A course lasts
for three days. During this time the people on the course build a
demonstration unit. Each person must pay the equivalent of US $1
for the course. (Experience has shown that when people have to pay
they do attend each day of the course.) Each person must also raise
money for his/her own construction materials.

CEMAT has now introduced this latrine also in Honduras and
Nicaragua.

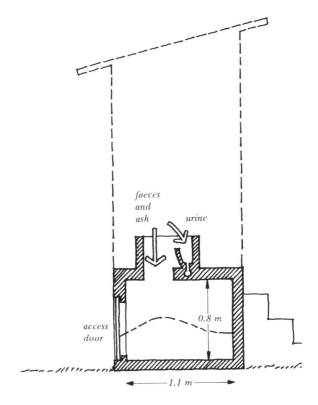

faeces
and
ash   *urine*

0.8 m

*access
door*

——— 1.1 m ———

Figure 18   A section (cut) through the Guatemalan latrine. Dimensions are
in metres

The only difference between the Vietnamese type and the Guatemalan type is the movable raised seat. This makes the latrine more expensive and complex to build but may in some areas be necessary for cultural reasons. An alternative to the movable raised seat is the baffle used in the example from Mexico (see figures 26 and 64).

The comments on the Vietnamese latrine at the end of section 3.3 apply also to the Guatemalan type. The advantage of taking the urine away from the receptacle is that its contents are more likely to remain dry and that there is no need to add kitchen and garden refuse.

3.5   India

In India the attitude to human excreta is different from that in China. With a few exceptions people do not use excreta to improve the soil. (Indirectly they do, as most people still defecate in the fields.)

Most Indians use water for anal cleaning and latrines often have a water seal as in figure 19. The amount of water needed for flushing is 2–3 litres.

Another possibility is to place the pit at some distance from the squatting slab and connect it with a 75 millimetre drainpipe or a covered brick channel. The pit is lined with a honeycomb of brick or stones. The lid must be tight-fitting to keep out insects and prevent odours. Where there is no risk of flooding, the lid may be slightly below ground level and covered with soil (see figure 20). In crowded places it is possible to place the pit under a footpath or even inside a house.

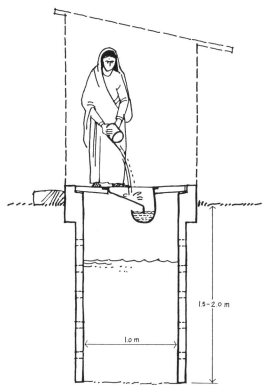

Figure 19   A pour-flush latrine with pan and water-seal trap directly above the pit. Dimensions are in metres

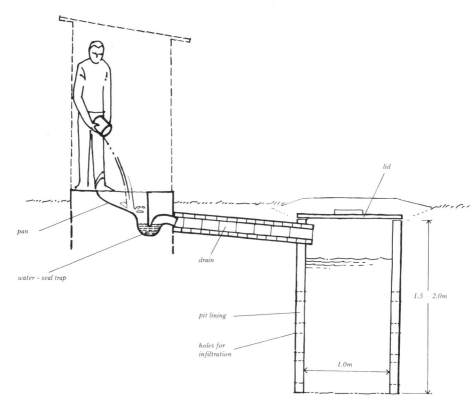

Figure 20   A section through a pour-flush latrine with the pit some distance
away from the squatting slab. Dimensions are in metres

After some years (depending on the volume of the pit, the nature
of the soil, the groundwater level and the number of users) the pit
fills up and has to be emptied. It is very unpleasant to empty a pit
with fresh excreta in it. For this reason it is good to have two pits.
The two pits are connected to the water seal with a Y-shaped drain
(see figure 21). By blocking one of the branches with a stone or a
brick at the Y-junction, the excreta are flushed into the other pit.

The double-pit pour-flush latrine has been developed over many
years and by several institutions. It is now propagated in India by the
UNDP Global Project for low-cost sanitation (Roy 1981).

The pits have a diameter of 1 metre and an effective depth of
1.0–1.5 metres. For a household of five persons, one pit takes three
to five years to fill up. The blockage at the Y-junction is then switched
so that the excreta are diverted into the second pit. The first pit is

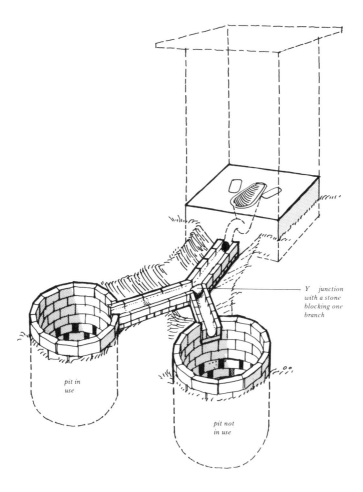

Figure 21 A pour-flush latrine with two pits. Drains and receptacles still to be
covered

left without use for two or three years and then emptied. The excreta
have by then turned into humus and may safely be used as manure.
The amount of manure collecting in a latrine of this type would be
about 50 litres per person per year.

The water-seal pour-flush latrine has several advantages: there
are no odours and no fly or mosquito breeding (if the lids of
the pits are tight-fitting!) and the excreta are out of sight.

It is unpleasant and hard work to empty a single-pit pour-flush latrine by hand. The contents are wet, smelly and dangerous to handle. With the double-pit version these problems are avoided.

Where there is little water, flushing is a problem. There may also be problems in areas with high groundwater table (India, Institute of Social Science Trust 1981).

Many other types of latrines -- with and without flushing -- have been developed in India. At the Gopuri Ashram in Maharashtra, Shri Appa Sahib Patwardhan and others developed several versions of the so-called Gopuri latrine (figure 22). It is a double-vault compost latrine similar to the Vietnamese type described earlier. The latrine has a ventpipe to remove odours and sometimes a sheet metal cover to increase the temperature inside the receptacle. Dry earth, ash, paddy husks, crushed dry leaves and straw are used to cover the faeces (Patel 1970).

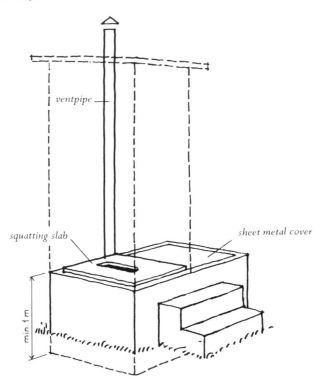

Figure 22   A Gopuri double-vault compost latrine. Dimensions are in metres

The Sopa Sandas is a double-vault compost latrine of different design (figure 23). The receptacle is not under the squatting slab but is on the side. The drop hole and the receptacle are connected via a chute like in the South African type described later in this chapter.

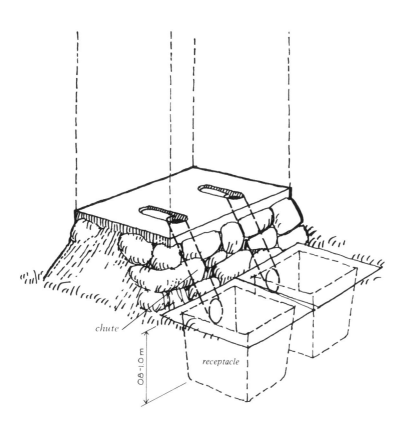

Figure 23   A Sopa Sandas double-vault compost latrine. Dimensions are in metres

At the receptacle end the chute is covered with a flap-trap, a hinged lid, preventing insects and rodents from entering the vault, or if they are inside, from leaving it.

The receptacle is a shallow, excavated pit divided into two chambers, each covered with a metal sheet. The sheet is removed when the receptacle is to be emptied (India, Central Public Health Engineering Research Institute 1964).

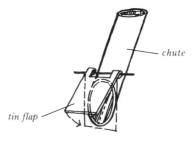

Figure 24   A latrine chute with a hinged lid (flap-trap)

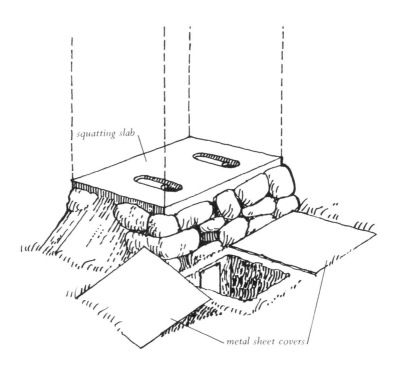

Figure 25   The Sopa Sandas latrine of figure 23 with one cover removed for
             access to the receptacle

The Gopuri and the Sopa Sandas latrines do not pollute soil or water. Those who empty the latrines do not have to handle fresh excreta.

Fly breeding is a possible problem with the Gopuri type. The Sopa Sandas is better in this respect. The flap-trap prevents flies from leaving the receptacle. The covers collect solar heat and increase the surface temperature of the pile so much that fly eggs cannot develop (see appendix 2, thermal control).

The Gopuri has almost no odours because of the ventpipe.

The receptacle should be large enough so that people can use one vault for at least six months.

3.6 Mexico

In several countries, readers of previous editions of *Sanitation without Water* have tried new types of latrines. In southern Mexico, for instance (in a low-cost housing project in the town of Merida), members of the Tecnologia Alternativa group have built solar-heated compost latrines.

Like the Gopuri and Sopa Sandas latrines in India, the Mexican type has a receptacle divided into two vaults. Above the dividing wall there is a baffle (see figure 26). The baffle directs the excreta into one vault. When that vault is full, the person looking after the latrine turns a handle. The excreta are then directed into the other vault.

This Mexican type has a fixed seat. There is a ventpipe which goes from the receptacle to above the roof. It takes away odours. If there is a screen on the top of the ventpipe, it acts as a fly trap (see section 6.14 and figure 94).

As you can see in figure 26, the receptacle is larger than the building above. The vaults have lids which are made of aluminium sheets, painted black. The lids face south (as Mexico is north of the Equator). This way they collect solar heat. This increases the evaporation from the receptacle as well as the temperature of the surface of the compost pile.

The vaults are only 0.75 metre wide but over 2 metres long. When the compost pile has reached the baffle, the person looking after the latrine can shift the pile to the lower end of the receptacle. This means that people need to empty the latrine only once a year at most (if 6-8 people are using it regularly).

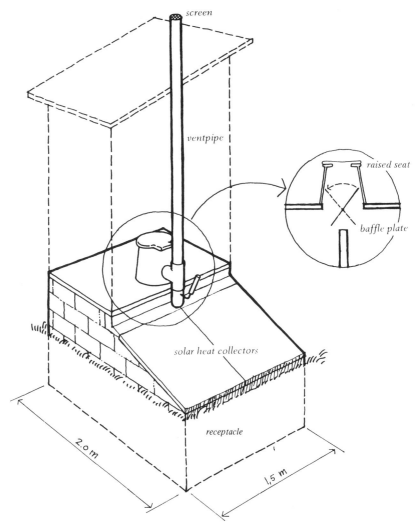

Figure 26   A double-vault compost latrine with solar-heated receptacle. Dimensions are in metres

This latrine is more expensive than the Indian types we de-scribed on previous pages. It is, however, a permanent structure, it can last for many years and it has a high capacity. It is easy to change from one vault to the other because of the baffle.

Because people leave the compost for more than a year and because of the higher temperatures (due to the solar heater), this compost latrine should achieve a high degree of pathogen destruction.

3.7 Sweden

The Multrum is a compost latrine consisting of a receptacle with a slanting floor, air conduits and at the lower end a storage chamber. A tube connects the toilet seat with the receptacle and there is often a special chute for kitchen refuse.

There is a constant draught due to natural convection from an air intake in the storage chamber, through the air conduits and out via a ventpipe. The ventpipe is at least 6 metres above the toilet seat or garbage opening, whichever is higher. (Some people put an exhaust fan in the ventpipe.)

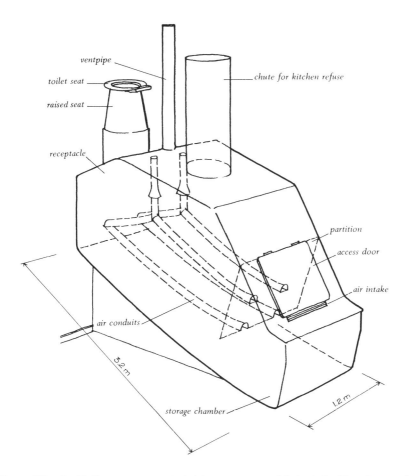

Figure 27 A Multrum compost latrine — a prefabricated fibreglass unit. Dimensions are in metres

Before you use a Multrum, you must cover the sloping floor (slope about 30°) with a starter bed. The bed consists of a 0.4 metre thick layer of peat moss and a 0.2 metre layer of garden soil rich in humus (not raw subsoil or clay). You should first mix the soil with grass cuttings. The purpose of this bed is to absorb liquids and to provide the microbes required for the oxidation of urine.

The Swedes put into the Multrum not only faeces and urine but all kinds of organic kitchen and household residues: vegetable and meat scraps, peelings, bones, eggshells, floor sweepings, sanitary napkins and grass clippings. They do not put the following into the Multrum: cans, glass, plastic or large amounts of liquids of any kind.

Because the floor of the Multrum slopes. the contents are slowly sliding from the fresh deposits at the upper end down to the storage part of the receptacle. The process of decomposition reduces the heap to less than 10% of the original volume.

The heap gradually becomes humus: a black, lumpy substance similar to good garden compost. It may take five years until a household has to take out the humus for the first time. After that they may have to take it out once a year. (The larger part of the receptacle is never emptied. Only material that has passed under the partition separating the storage chamber from the rest of the receptacle is removed.) The amount of humus varies from 10 to 30 litres per person per year.

The maximum number of users depends on factors such as temperature, humidity, amount and type of refuse, proportion of urine to faeces, and volume of the receptacle. In most cases 8-10 people are the maximum for one Multrum unit in regular. year-round use.

The humus from the Multrum has a similar bacterial content to soil. The Swedes consider it safe to use directly as a fertilizer and soil conditioner.

You can buy various types of Multrum in Scandinavia, in the USA and in Canada. Here we show the largest one, the Clivus Multrum. It has a volume of 3–4 cubic metres. The Swedes usually put it in a basement directly under the bathroom and kitchen.

If you are using the Multrum as an outside toilet. you can place it in a shallow pit and build a shelter above it (figure 29).

From an ecological point of view, the Multrum is close to the ideal. There is no pollution of soil or water. The only things that go into the air are carbon dioxide and water vapour.

From a health point of view, the Multrum is not as safe as a

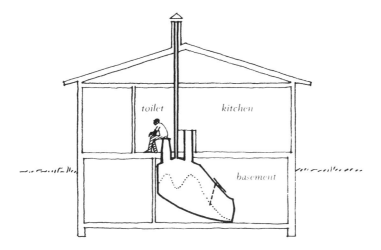

Figure 28   A Multrum latrine installed in the basement of a house

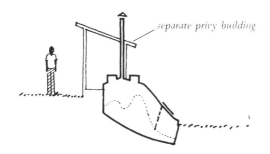

Figure 29   A Multrum latrine installed outdoors

double-vault latrine. The reason for this is that pathogenic organisms can be washed down from the top of the pile to the storage part of the receptacle. (This cannot happen in a double-vault latrine as there is a solid wall between the two vaults.) Fly breeding is another possible problem.

If people have built their Multrum properly and look after it well, then it is reasonably nuisance-free. If the Multrum is inside the house, then fruit flies may cause a problem. On still, humid days there may be odour. If the Multrum is away from the house, then there will not be such problems.

The cost of a prefabricated fibreglass Multrum is far above what would be feasible in a developing country. Present prices in Scandinavia and North America range from US $1000 to 2000, not including installation.

3.8   Yemen

In the old part of the city of Sanaa, as in other Yemeni towns, the houses are tall and slender, rising five to nine storeys from narrow streets. A house is usually occupied by one extended family. Each floor has one or two lavatory–bathrooms next to a vertical shaft. As figure 30 shows, this shaft runs from the top of the house to a receptacle at the level of the street.

The faeces drop through a hole in the squatting slab, down the shaft, to the receptacle. An employee of a public bath-house empties the receptacle frequently and takes the contents to the bath.

Sanaa has 18 public baths, the oldest dating back to mediaeval times. The baths are used by almost everyone once a week. They are run by hereditary bath-keepers who charge a small fee for their use.

At the bath-house the faeces are spread out on the roof to dry. Wood is scarce in Sanaa and the dried faeces are therefore used as fuel together with skins and bones from the slaughter yards.

The ashes from the bath-house fires are sold as fertilizer for the orchards and vegetable gardens in town.

The urine drains away from the squatting slab to a groove in the stone floor. From there it goes through an opening in the wall of the house, down a vertical drainage surface on the outer face of the building. (These surfaces are often elegantly shaped and decorated.) As soon as it reaches the ground, the part of the liquid not evaporated on the way disappears into a soakpit.

Anal cleaning takes place on a pair of square stones next to the squatting slab. The used water is drained away in the same way as the urine. No liquids are thus led into the long drop shaft or the receptacle below. As Sanaa has a hot, dry climate, the faeces quickly dry out (Kirkman 1976, Lewcock 1976).

Next to the latrine there is a charcoal fire in a bucket. After anal cleaning, the Yemenites dry themselves by squatting over the bucket (De Cal 1984 personal communication).

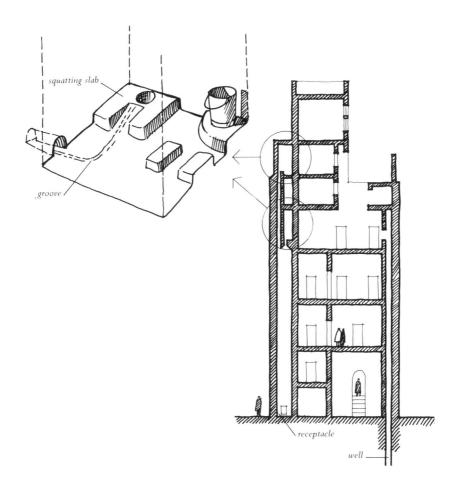

squatting slab

groove

receptacle

well

Figure 30   A section through a tall building in Sanaa, North Yemen. The latrines on the upper floors have a common chute to a receptacle at street level

This system may seem strange, but it is very suitable for the local situation: tall buildings, extremely dry climate, not much water and no firewood. It is good because there is no pollution of water or soil.

One problem is that those who empty the receptacles come into contact with fresh excreta. While the faeces are drying on the roof of the bath, flies may reach them. However, the faeces are very dry and flies usually do not lay eggs in material with less than 65% moisture.

The final disposal of ashes is safe, as burning efficiently destroys all pathogenic organisms.

3.9   Algeria

The conditions in the town of Ouargla in the Algerian desert are in some ways similar to those of Sanaa in Yemen. The climate is hot and dry, the houses are close together, streets are narrow and the whole town was until recently surrounded by a wall. Most houses are two or three floors high. The groundwater table is very high. It may reach within 0.3 metre of the ground surface.

The traditional system of excreta disposal in Ouargla is compost latrines. The latrine is inside the house against a wall that faces the street. The latrine consists of a squatting slab above a shallow receptacle at or slightly below street level. From the latrine on the first floor, there is a long drop chute to the same receptacle.

People put palm leaves in the receptacle to help make compost from the excreta. The receptacle is emptied from an opening in the street.

Figure 31   A latrine receptacle at street level. The opening is blocked with stones

The cobble-stones which cover the hole in the wall are removed and the contents are put in baskets and carried away. The compost is sold and used as a soil conditioner and fertilizer for date palm plantations outside the town wall (Asklund *et al.* 1972).

This system will not cause pollution. However, there is a health problem. This is because the latrines are single-vault latrines. In the receptacle there is compost, but there are also fresh excreta. When people empty the receptacles, they may come in contact with fresh excreta. For health reasons it is better to have two vaults, which people use alternately.

3.10   Ladakh (India)

We can also find long drop systems (with or without composting) in the Himalayas and Tibet.

Ladakh is a dry highland region in the western Himalayas. Most of it belongs to India, but culturally and geographically it is Tibetan. In Ladakh most houses have indoor latrines which are on the upper floors.

On the floor of a small room next to the kitchen/living room there is a thick layer of soil from the garden. In the floor a drop hole leads to a small ground-floor room. This room can only be reached from the outside. People excrete on the soil which is on the floor. Then they push soil and excreta together down the drop hole. They may also add ashes from the kitchen above. The household members bring loads of soil into the room when necessary. For the long winter a supply is piled into one corner of the latrine room upstairs. A spade or shovel is also kept in the room. Normally there is no anal cleaning.

The entrance of the ground-floor room is blocked with stones or fitted with a door. The decomposed excreta are removed in spring and when summer is over and spread on the fields.

The system is good, but it may mean that people handle fresh excreta. An answer to the problem is to make two holes in the floor: one for winter, one for summer.

For a country where water is in short supply in summer and frozen in winter this is a very clever system. The soil/excreta mixture is a valuable soil conditioner, especially in Ladakh where

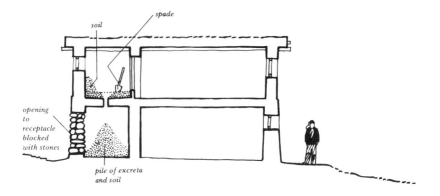

Figure 32   Section through a Ladakhi house with an indoor, upper-floor earth
            latrine

there is little topsoil and all animal manure is used as fuel.

As long as the latrine is well maintained and enough soil is put in every day, there are no odours. In some cases there is a faint smell of ammonia from urine splashed on the soil-covered floor of the latrine room. There is no fly breeding.

The system does not work well in the central part of the town of Leh where people have no easy access to soil.

3.11   Bhutan

Bhutan is in the eastern Himalayas. It has a small and scattered population. The traditional farmhouse is a remarkable piece of architecture of great beauty. It is built of rammed earth, stones and timber. It usually has two or three floors. Pigs, cows and horses are on the ground floor. The next floor is used as a store and people live on the upper floor(s). People enter the house by a steep ladder that goes to an upstairs platform. Another ladder goes up to the living area through a trap-door.

The latrine consists of a hole in the floor of the entrance platform and/or first-floor balcony. The excreta fall on the ground or on the floor of an enclosed pig-pen. People use short pieces of twigs for anal cleaning.

Figure 33   A long drop latrine in Bhutan

There are also improved versions of this latrine. The Jambelhagang monastery in Bumthang has a first-floor latrine with a wooden chute (0.25 × 0.25 metre internally). This leads to a receptacle made of stone at ground level. In Ura village, east of Bumthang, some of the traditional farmhouses have a stone receptacle which goes from the ground 3–4 metres up to the first floor balcony.

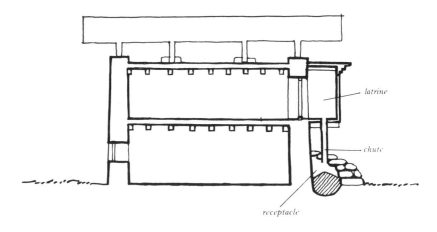

Figure 34   A section through the latrine and the house in figure 33

With the open type of latrine, faeces do not usually pile up. This is because the pigs, dogs and rats eat them immediately. This means that there are no odours, nor any human excreta for the flies to breed in. However, it is possible that tapeworms may spread (see section 2.2). Another problem is that the hole is small and the wood around it becomes soiled. Therefore, hookworms may breed on the entrance platform or the latrine balcony.

The Bhutanese latrines are well suited to local conditions: the use of solid materials for anal cleaning and the keeping of pigs on the ground floor. With high buildings, steep ladders, bitterly cold nights in winter and bears prowling around the houses in summer, upstairs sanitation is a matter of necessity.

3.12 West Germany

We can also find the long drop system in Europe according to a German handbook on masonry construction (Behringer 1959). Unlike the Yemeni system, the German long drop latrine does not separate urine and faeces. The receptacle is water-tight. It can hold 500 litres per person per year. It is necessary to pump out the contents when the receptacle is full.

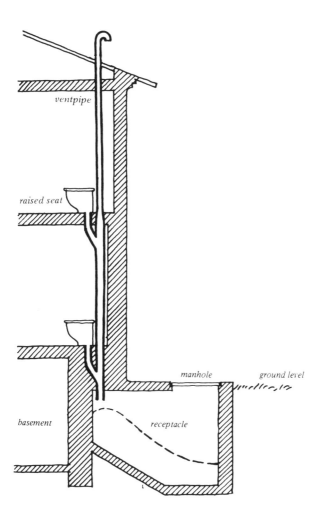

Figure 35   A section through a long drop latrine in Germany

The German system is not as good as the Yemeni system. This is because the contents of the receptacle are liquid. Thus it is necessary to use a pump to empty the receptacle.

However, it would be possible to change the German system into a compost latrine.

3.13   Tanzania

In many parts of the world, people use the pit latrine. In its simplest form it consists of a large pit, which people dig by hand. On top of the pit there is a squatting slab made of timber and soil (see figure 36).

In Tanzania, the pit is often 1 metre wide, 2 metres long and 3–4 metres deep. It has a simple shelter on top. The shelter may consist of a screen wall only. When the pit is full, people dig another pit nearby and make a new shelter.

Into the pit goes excreta plus cleaning material. Muslims and most people along the coast and in other Muslim dominated areas use water for anal cleaning. Other people use banana leaves or other leaves, grass, corncobs, paper, etc.

This simple latrine has good points. Its function is clear. Where soil and water conditions are right, people can easily make a pit latrine from local materials.

There are also bad points. The pit latrine needs special conditions. People sometimes forget these and there are bad results. The pit latrine needs soil which is deep, stable and permeable. If the soil is not stable, the pit will collapse. This can happen after heavy rains.

The pit must be above the groundwater table. If it is not (or if the soil is impermeable) water will collect in the pit. Then mosquitoes will breed.

Filth flies also breed in the pit. The soil on the platform acts as a breeding place for hookworms. The odours from the pit can be very bad. The pit often only lasts for a few years.

Under favourable circumstances the pit latrine can be an excellent solution to problems of excreta disposal. For instance, at Omdurman in the Sudan there are latrines that have been in use from time immemorial. Some pits are over 20 metres deep. But it is a rare exception. Frequently the traditional pit latrine is a health hazard and a nuisance.

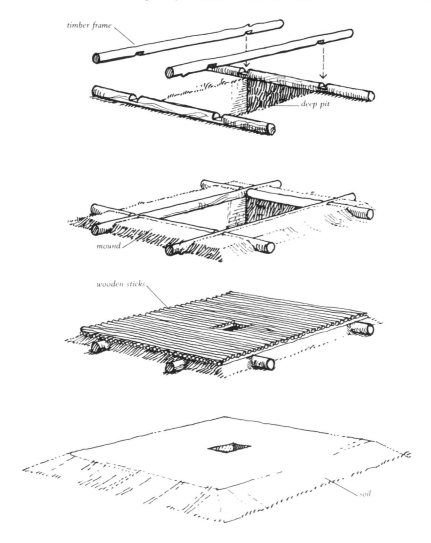

Figure 36   A squatting slab made of timber and soil

3.14   Zimbabwe

In Harare, Zimbabwe, the Blair Research Laboratory developed an improved type of pit latrine in the mid-1970s. It is called the 'Ventilated Improved Pit' (VIP) latrine. More than 30 000 such latrines have now been built in Zimbabwe (Morgan and Mara 1982).

The VIP latrine has a squatting slab made of reinforced concrete.

The slab covers a deep pit, which is 1.5 metres wide. The pit is partly lined. The slab has two openings: a squat hole and a vent hole. Around the squat hole there is a shelter. The vent hole is outside the shelter.

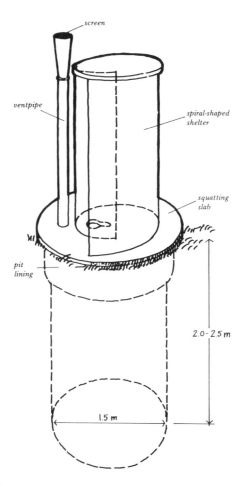

Figure 37   A VIP latrine

The vent hole is fitted with a pipe, 150 millimetres in diameter and about 2.5 metres high. The pipe is painted black and it is on the sunny side of the latrine. The top of the pipe is cone-shaped and opens out to 200 millimetres. The opening is covered with a copper or fibreglass fly screen. According to a recent publication (Ryan and Mara 1983), it is not necessary to paint the ventpipe black, nor to make it cone-shaped at the top.

When there is a difference of temperature between the inside and the outside of the pipe, there will be a draught of air up the pipe. This will draw air and gases from the pit. As a result there will be a draught of air down through the squat hole.

Flies from outside are attracted to the odours passing up the pipe, and so do not come into the shelter. Because of the screen on the pipe, the flies cannot enter the pit. As a result there is less fly breeding in the pit. Any flies which do breed in the pit are attracted by the light at the top of the pipe. However, because of the screen, they cannot get out. They are trapped. After a while they die, and fall back into the pit.

We can see from this that it is important for the shelter to be a little bit dark, so that the flies inside the pit are attracted to the stronger light in the pipe. The Zimbabweans have found that the best shelter is spiral-shaped, without a door (see figure 37). Walls and roofs are made of ferrocement (see page 122) or any locally available materials (see also chapter 8).

This improved latrine has several advantages over the traditional type. Because the pit is partly lined, there is less risk that the pit will collapse. The concrete slab can be cleaned and does not provide a breeding ground for hookworms. The ventpipe makes the latrine particularly odour-free and reduces fly breeding.

There are some problems, however. It is not good to use this latrine where the groundwater table is high. This latrine cannot be built where the ground is rocky. When the pit fills up, it is necessary to build a new latrine. *Culex* mosquitoes will breed in the pit if it turns wet. There is a lining around the top of the pit, but it might still collapse. On the whole, however the VIP latrine is a considerable improvement over the traditional pit latrine.

3.15   Botswana

The Ministry of Local Government and Lands in Botswana, together with the Building Research Establishment in the UK, has developed a double-vault ventilated pit latrine for use in squatter areas and site and service schemes. The type we describe here, the 'Revised Earth Closet II' (REC II), also known as the VIDP latrine, has been used in urban areas in Botswana since 1978 (van Nostrand and Wilson 1983). About 10 000 units have been built in Botswana over the past six years (J. Gadek 1984, personal communication).

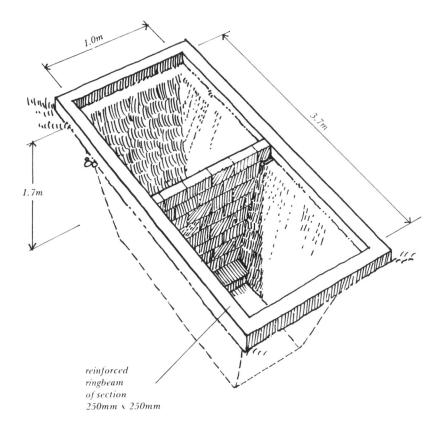

Figure 38   The double vault receptacle of an REC II latrine. Dimensions are in metres and millimetres

The REC II latrine consists of a shallow pit divided into two vaults. Each vault has an effective volume of 1.5 cubic metres. When built in stable soil the pit is not lined. There is a beam around the top of the pit and this supports slabs and covers. In unstable soil the pit is lined with solid concrete blocks of thickness 150 millimetres on a concrete foundation which is 200 millimetres deep and 400 millimetres wide. There is then no beam around the top. The covers are made of precast concrete and they are removable. Sometimes a sealing compound is applied to the joints between the covers.

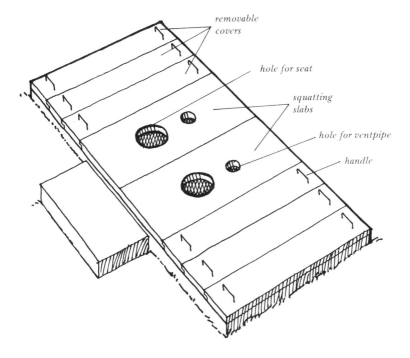

Figure 39   The receptacle of figure 38 provided with squatting slabs and covers

There is a drop hole above each vault. The hole that is in use has a seat. The other hole has a tight-fitting lid. For each receptacle there is a screened ventpipe.

The latrine has been designed for use in densely built-up areas where it is not always possible to dig a new pit when the old one is full. The REC II is a permanent unit that can be emptied either manually or mechanically on a 3–4 year cycle. The pit contents can be used as soil conditioner and fertilizer.

In the Botswana project the municipal councils provide the latrine itself to each plot of land. The plot owner pays back the cost over a 15-year period. He must build the latrine shelter himself and he must provide the latrine with a fibreglass seat unit (made locally).

The REC II is a cross between the double-vault compost latrine and the pit latrine. Like the compost latrine it has the advantage of being permanent. The shallow pit is easier to dig and to empty

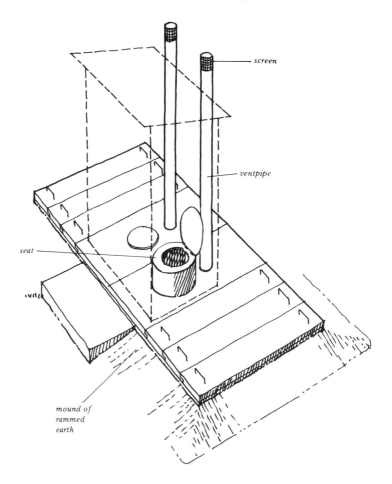

Figure 40   The REC II latrine with seat and ventpipes. The hole not in use has a
            tight-fitting lid

than the much deeper pit of an ordinary latrine. When the
receptacle is lined the pit can be even shallower as the receptacle
can be extended above ground (compare this with the Mexican
example in figure 26).

In Botswana, people use it like an ordinary pit latrine. This
means that the contents of the receptacle turn wet. An alternative
would be to use it as a compost latrine by adding some soil,
lime, ash, husks or sawdust every day.

The Botswana project has not yet been evaluated but when
visiting Gaborone in mid-1984 we noticed that a number of

unlined pits had collapsed. We also noticed that many people use the second vault for refuse. This makes it difficult for the municipal vacuum truck to empty the vault. The households must be better informed about how the double-vault latrine is to be used. The lid over the unused vault must be fixed so that it cannot easily be removed.

3.16   South Africa

ROEC stands for 'Reid's Odourless Earth Closet' and is a type of improved pit latrine developed in South Africa and patented in 1944. The pit is 1 metre wide, 2 metres long and at least 3 metres deep. It is covered with a concrete slab and fitted with a 75 millimetre diameter ventpipe. The squatting slab is on the side of the receptacle as shown in figure 41.

The excreta enter the pit through a chute. Only excreta and toilet paper go into the pit. The chute does not have a lid.

The contents of the receptacle gradually decompose. The soil soaks up liquids. The ventpipe takes away odours. Fresh air is sucked down the chute.

The pit fills up slowly as long as the soil remains permeable. A receptacle with the dimensions given above and with no more than six regular users may last for up to 20 years.

It is possible to attach the ROEC latrine to a house via a ventilated passage. In some cases it is possible to place it in the house, with the pit outside the wall. This is possible as a properly constructed and well maintained ROEC latrine is completely free from odours.

An unlined pit needs a slight inward slope towards the bottom. The slope should be 80–100 millimetres per metre depth. Holes are necessary in the lining in order for liquids to soak away.

Around the top of the pit is a collar described in detail in chapter 8. The collar supports the cover slab of the receptacle. It is essential that the entire receptacle, collar and cover slab are completely air-tight and that the slab makes an air-tight joint on the collar of the pit. Any method of construction of this air-tight cover slab may be used provided it is strong enough.

In South Africa some of the components are prefabricated in asbestos cement: ventpipe, chute, squatting slab and seat. The vent-pipe can be made from any non-corrosive material as long as it is

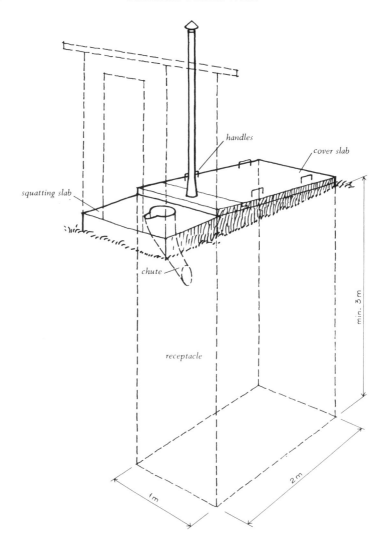

Figure 41   An ROEC latrine. Dimensions are in metres

air-tight. The chute can be made from a piece of drainpipe as shown in figure 108.

Before anyone uses an ROEC latrine for the first time, it should be tested for possible air leaks. This can be done by placing a bundle of dry grass, newspaper or cotton waste soaked in oil on the floor of the receptacle, directly below the chute. (This must be done before the cover slab is fitted over the pit.) The bundle can be lit by dropping a piece of lighted paper down the chute. When the fire in the pit is burning properly, smoke will flow out of the top of the ventpipe, and there will be a downdraught in the chute. If there is smoke coming up the chute, then there is a leak in the system. It is important to find and seal all leaks (Bells Asbestos & Engineering Africa Ltd, undated).

The ROEC latrine has the good points of a traditional pit latrine. In addition it has some advantages: it is completely free from odours, the user cannot see the contents of the pit, there is no lid to replace, there is nothing to put in apart from the excreta, and the latrine is not supposed to be emptied.

The patent holder claims that the ROEC latrine is 'absolutely free from flies provided that no decomposed or other fly-blown matter is put into the pit'. Our tests in Tanzania do not agree with this. Fly breeding is quite possible in the pit of an ROEC latrine. It is possible to reduce the problem by providing the ventpipe with a fly screen.

If liquids collect in the pit there is a risk of mosquito breeding.

The chute makes it possible for rodents to move into and out of the receptacle. This could be prevented if the chute has a flap-trap similar to the one used in the Sopa Sandas in India (see figure 24).

As with all deep pit latrines, the risk of collapse is great, even with a lined pit.

3.17 USA

The United States, Treasury Department, Public Health Service (1933) published a handbook on latrine building called *The sanitary privy*. It claimed to include designs which represented the best sanitary privy practices in the various states.

The 'earth-pit privy' as recommended in the USA 50 years ago can be seen as a luxury model of the traditional pit latrine. The more subtle details of its construction are well described by Charles Sale (1929) in *The Specialist*.

The receptacle is a dug-out, 1 × 1 metre square and at least 1.5 metres deep. The pit has a wooden curbing extending 0.15–0.20 metre above the original ground level. The curbing lines the whole

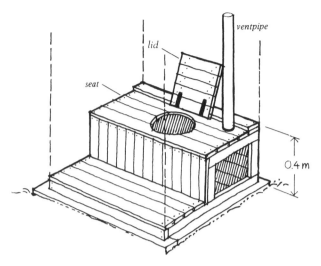

Figure 42   The earth-pit privy — a VIP latrine developed in the USA over 50
            years ago. Dimensions are in metres

of the pit. If the soil is very stable, then the curbing need only line
the upper part. The first three upper boards of the curb siding must
be tight. The lower boards can be 20–30 millimetres apart.

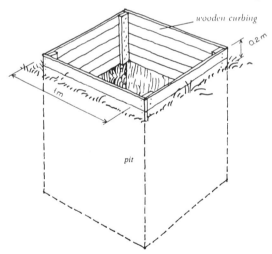

Figure 43   Wooden curbing of the upper part of the pit. Dimensions are in
            metres

Around the top of the curbing there is a mound. The mound begins
on the same level as the curbing, and then slopes away from it. This
is so that surface water will not enter the pit. The mound is at least

0.5 metre wide on each side. The mound is rammed with a piece of solid timber as shown in figure 44.

The platform and seat are made from tongue-and-groove timber in order to make them insect-tight. Note in the illustration (figure 42) that the boards are placed vertically on the front of the raised seat. This makes sure that urine is carried down into the pit and does not leak through, as might happen if the boards were laid horizontally.

Figure 44   A mound of rammed earth prevents surface water from entering the pit

There is also a hinged lid and a ventpipe, as shown in figure 42. (The hinges are made from strips cut out of the side walls of an old car tyre.) The seat often had two or more holes, frequently made to accommodate persons of different sizes.

Compared to the traditional pit latrine of Tanzania type the 'earth-pit privy' has the advantages of being non-collapsible due to the pit lining and less odorous due to the ventpipe. The other problems remain. The raised seat has no advantages from a health point of view.

3.18   Egypt

A variation of the borehole latrine was developed in south-east Asia 50 years ago (Carter 1938), and has since been used in many countries including Egypt.

The receptacle is a vertical hole with a diameter of about 0.4 metre and a depth of 6 metres. It is bored in the ground with an auger as shown in figure 45. The wooden auger guide is not essential but simplifies the operations.

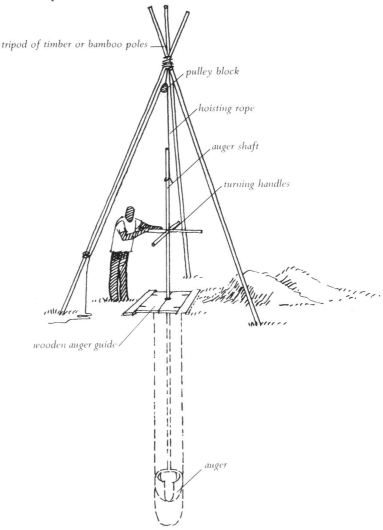

tripod of timber or bamboo poles

pulley block

hoisting rope

auger shaft

turning handles

wooden auger guide

auger

Figure 45   Digging a borehole latrine

Around the top of the hole there is a collar of concrete or some other impervious material. Its purpose is to support the weight of the slab, to prevent the edges of the hole from caving in and to prevent fly breeding in the earth under the slab.

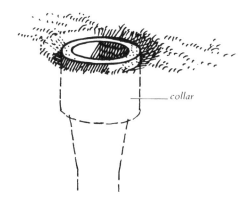

Figure 46   The upper part of the borehole must be fitted with a collar – here a piece of concrete pipe

The hole is covered with a squatting slab as shown in figure 47.

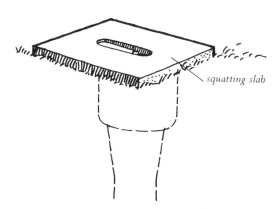

Figure 47   A squatting slab fitted above the borehole

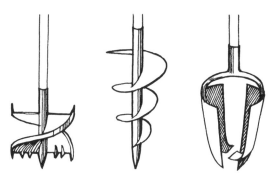

Figure 48   Different types of augers used for digging borehole latrines

The auger should be around 0.4 metre in diameter. If it is much smaller, then users can easily make the side walls of the hole dirty. If the auger is larger, then it is more difficult to turn. Various types of augers can be used for digging borehole latrines.

The subsoil must be sufficiently firm so that it will not cave in, yet soft enough to allow easy cutting by the auger. Caving in is frequent with this type of latrine, especially in sandy or alluvial soils. In such cases it is necessary to give the bored hole a lining. The lining must not cover the side walls completely, however. This is because contact between the side walls and the excreta is important for the decomposition process.

A dry latrine 0.4 metre wide and 6 metres deep fills up in less than two years if used regularly by 5–6 people. The life of a latrine reaching down into the groundwater table can be much longer. In Egypt there are many that have been in regular use for more than eight years (Carter 1938).

The borehole latrine has much the same advantages and disadvantages as the ordinary pit latrine. Its lifetime is even shorter and it needs special construction equipment not usually available to individual households.

The 'long-life' type with a wet borehole carries with it the risks of mosquito breeding and groundwater pollution.

The often-repeated statement that filth flies do not breed in deep, dark holes is not correct. Fly breeding can thus be a serious problem in this type of latrine.

4 SELECTING THE RIGHT LATRINE

The examples in chapter 3 show how many different possibilities there are.

Which system is best?

There is no such thing as a 'best' latrine suitable for all conditions everywhere. We need a range of possibilities. What we select depends on our local situation.

The first choice should be between the use of a flush system or a drop system. The way in which we decide between these is shown in figure 49(a) on the next page. If we have to use a drop system, our second choice must be whether to use a pit latrine or a compost latrine. Figure 49(b) on page 61 shows how we make this decision.

Sometimes when we try to answer the questions posed in figures 49(a) and 49(b), it is not possible to give a clear YES or NO. In such cases it may be necessary to discuss the questions in more detail. We shall do this later in this chapter, starting on page 62.

4.1   Flush system or drop system?

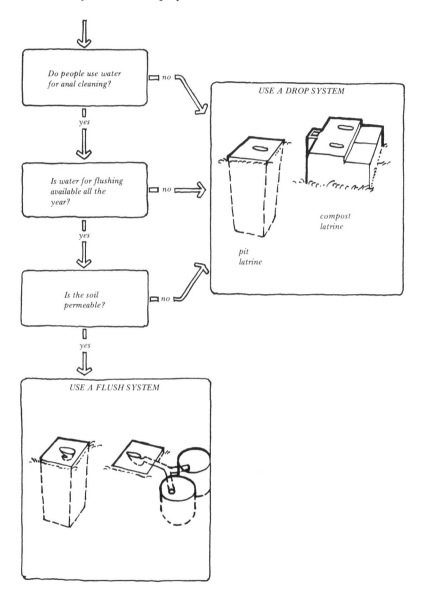

Figure 49(a)   A flush system or a drop system?

If the answer to all these questions is YES, select a flush system. If the answer to one of the questions is NO, choose a pit latrine or a compost latrine.

4.2 Pit latrine or compost latrine?

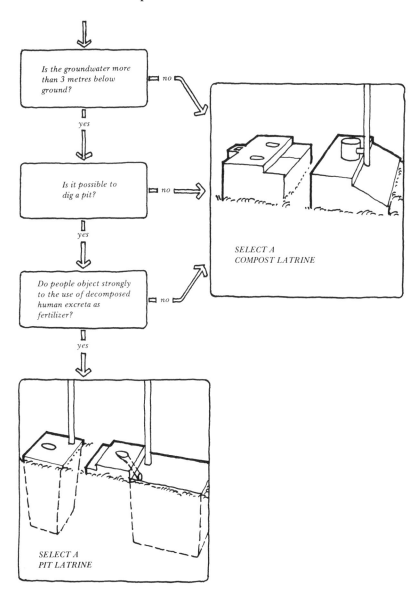

Figure 49(b) A pit latrine or a compost latrine?

If the answer to all the second set of questions is YES, choose a pit latrine. If the answer to any one of the questions is NO, choose a compost latrine.

4.3   Do people use water for anal cleaning?

In some cultures people are 'washers', that is, they use water for anal cleaning. In other cultures they are 'wipers', using some solid material like grass, leaves, paper, sticks, corncobs, mudballs or stones. For the washers a flush system may work well. But if the wipers use a flush system, then the solid cleaning material will clog water seals and drainpipes.

Bhutan shows clearly what can happen when a technology is transferred from one culture to another. The majority of people in Bhutan are wipers with traditional latrines of drop type. In spite of this, during the last 10–20 years, flush systems according to Indian standards have been put into most schools, hospitals, offices and many houses. The result has been disastrous, especially at schools and hospitals. The drains are permanently clogged, the flush pans are full. Even worse, faeces are present all over the floors of toilet cubicles, in nearby corridors and washrooms and outdoors on the ground around the buildings. The reason for this terrible state of affairs is not faulty design or construction. The fault is that the wrong system has been used. Flush systems can only work if all users always use water for anal cleaning. To change cultural patterns – in this case turning wipers into washers – is not easy, and would in any case take a long time.

Perhaps using toilet paper for wiping instead of solid material might have solved the problem. But this is not really possible in Bhutan. Toilet paper must be imported and is not always available. The price of one small roll is equivalent to half a day's wages for an unskilled labourer.

The situation in Bhutan is not unique. Similar problems occur in other parts of the world, particularly in Africa where washers and wipers exist side by side.

4.4   Is water for flushing available all the year?

Flushing takes at least 2–3 litres of water every time someone uses a latrine. If this water is not readily available, then a flush system will not work. Even communities that normally have enough water may periodically have serious shortages. In such a case, it is impossible to use a flush latrine. But there would be no problem in using a drop latrine.

4.5   Is the soil permeable?

Certain subsoil conditions make it impossible or extremely costly to construct a pit. Such conditions are, for example, bedrock and impermeable or always waterlogged soil. But you may be able to cope with the problem if you change the design of the pit. Instead of one deep pit, you can have two shallow pits. It is often possible to raise the upper part of the receptacle (pit) above ground. You can build a compost latrine entirely above ground.

4.6   Is the groundwater more than 3 metres below ground?

If the pit reaches down into the groundwater, the effective volume (that is, the part of the pit you can use) is smaller. A more serious problem is mosquito breeding in the foul water of a pit latrine. Mosquitoes can also breed in a water-seal latrine if the covers of drains, inspection chamber and pit are not tight-fitting. When wet pits are introduced in an area that did not have latrines before, the *Culex* mosquito population is likely to increase a great deal (see section 2.5). In practice, it is nearly impossible to build and maintain latrines in such a way that mosquitoes cannot get in and out. The best way to control mosquito breeding in a latrine is to keep the receptacle dry. This is not possible with a flush system, but can be done with a drop system.

There are other aspects to consider though. A periodic increase in groundwater level may have beneficial effects on a pit. The pit walls are declogged and the absorptive capacity of the soil is restored.

Some authors (Morgan and Mara 1982) claim that pit latrines should be wet and even recommend that people use VIP-type latrines as washrooms. A wet pit is said to take longer to fill up than a dry pit (Wagner and Lanoix 1958). This advantage has to be weighed against the increased mosquito breeding that is likely to be the result of introducing wet pits into area where there is a long dry season.

4.7 Do people object strongly to the use of decomposed human excreta as fertilizer?

Many cultures regard human excreta as an unpleasant and dangerous waste product and refuse to handle them even when decomposed. Under such conditions a final deposit system (like a pit latrine) would be suitable. Others view the excreta as a valuable resource and may even be prepared to pay to collect them. For such cultures a compost latrine is acceptable.

There is a further consideration.

When the children being born today are adults. the world will have two or three times as many people as now. There will not be more land. In order to feed these people we must make use of all resources. These include human excreta.

4.8 Costs

We have not included cost considerations in this chapter. The reason is that final costs depend more on the choice of materials and production methods than on the type of latrine selected. An owner-builder using locally available materials like timber poles and reeds may be able to complete his latrine without any monetary costs or with only a small outlay for a factory-produced flush pan, a bag of cement or a fly screen. If all the components are purchased and labour is hired, the cost of even a simple latrine may exceed the equivalent of US $100.

5   LOCATION

Before you build your latrine, consider the following points about location:

- The position in relation to wells.
- The condition of the subsoil.
- The direction of the wind.
- Space available.

5.1   Make sure you will not pollute groundwater and wells

Make sure the receptacle is more than 1.5 metres above the highest groundwater table and that the soil is uniform and free from cracks. If the bottom of the receptacle is close to, or reaches down into, the groundwater, then place the latrine downhill from the well. If you cannot place the latrine downhill, then place it at least 15 metres away from the well. If the soil is sandy, however, you can place the latrine as close as 7.5 metres to a well built household well, if it is impossible to place it at a greater distance (Wagner and Lanoix 1958).

5.2   Where to locate a latrine in an area with fissured rocks or limestone formations

If you live in such an area, then you must place the latrine downhill from the well. This is because pollution from the latrine may travel long distances through fissured (cracked) rock and limestone.

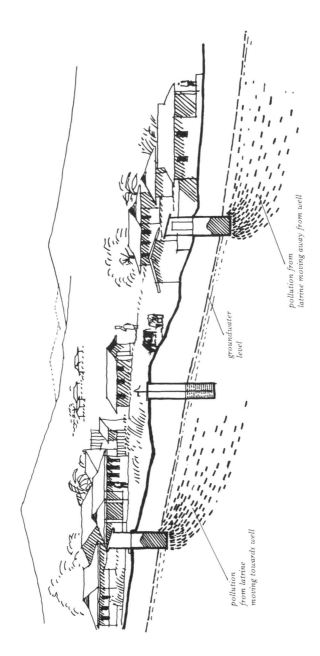

Figure 50   Movement of pollution in groundwater

5.3 Where to locate your latrine in relation to the direction of the wind

If your latrine has a ventpipe, make sure that nearby trees do not obstruct the flow of wind across the top of the ventpipe. The vent-pipe should preferably be on the windy side of the shelter. Doors and/or windows in the shelter should face the wind to increase the wind speed in the ventpipe (Ryan and Mara 1983).

5.4 Consider privacy and convenience

If you have a large plot of land, then it is best to place the latrine about 10–20 metres away from the house. If you place it further away, then perhaps people will not use it, and you may find it diffi-cult to look after. Also, strangers may use it.

In crowded urban areas you may have no choice. You must place the latrine close to or inside the house. If the latrine has a water seal or the receptacle is ventilated, then you will not have a problem from odour. One problem, however, will be insects. Most latrines in the tropics are full of cockroaches (as are most septic tanks). As long as the cockroaches stay inside the receptacle, then they are good, because they help decomposition. But they often find their way to the kitchen. Therefore you may prefer to place your latrine as far from the kitchen as possible.

6 LATRINE COMPONENTS

A latrine consists of a number of parts which people can combine in various ways. The basic parts are receptacle, squatting slab (with drop hole or flush pan) and shelter. These three parts are always there. In addition, a latrine can have one or more optional parts: aerator, baffle, fly trap, footrests, handle, lid, seat, solar heat collector, urine collector, water-seal trap and ventpipe.

6.1 Receptacle

The purpose of the receptacle is to receive and safely store the excreta and anything else which people normally put in it.

Size and shape can vary considerably from one type of latrine to another. It can be shallow like the Chinese one described in chapter 3. Someone must empty such a receptacle every day and take the excreta to a compost heap. Or the receptacle can be extremely deep like the traditional pit latrines of Omdurman in the Sudan. Because they have a depth of more than 20 metres they need not be emptied. In between these extremes there is a range of receptacles that we can choose from.

A *shallow receptacle* is a place to keep excreta for a short time. A shallow receptacle is normally used for compost latrines where the excreta are mixed with kitchen and/or garden residues. Someone must empty the receptacle at regular intervals. How often it is emptied depends on the number of users, on what goes into the receptacle, and on the size of the receptacle.

People usually make shallow receptacles out of masonry: stones, building blocks, sun-dried bricks, soil–cement blocks, concrete blocks, burnt bricks. It is possible to use wood also.

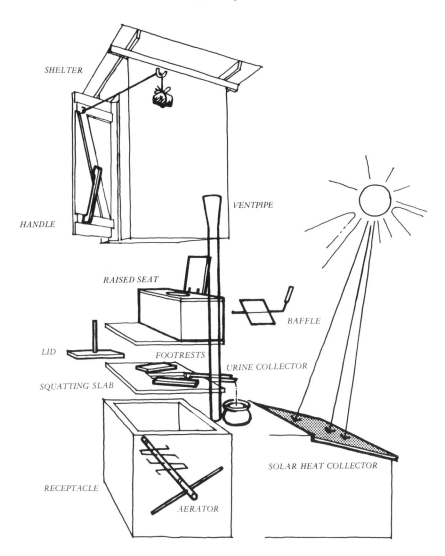

SHELTER

HANDLE

VENTPIPE

RAISED SEAT

BAFFLE

LID

FOOTRESTS

URINE COLLECTOR

SQUATTING SLAB

SOLAR HEAT COLLECTOR

RECEPTACLE

AERATOR

Figure 51   Latrine components

It is not necessary to make the walls water-tight, but they have to be tight enough to stop insects and rodents getting in or out. They must also be strong enough to carry the squatting slab, the user and the shelter.

The shallow receptacle can be 'closed', with no liquids going into the soil, or 'open', that is with the bottom being subsoil.

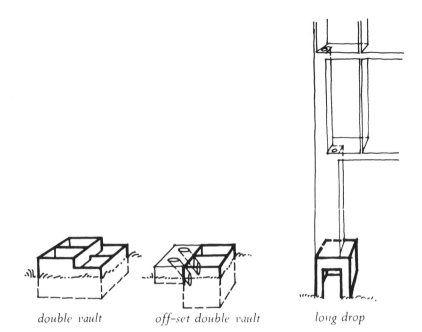

double vault   *off-set double vault*   *long drop*

Figure 52   Shallow receptacles

The double-vault receptacle in figure 52 is a development of the Indian Gopuri type and the Vietnamese type. You can empty this receptacle from above via a removable cover. This means that you can place the receptacle as low as the groundwater allows.

We find the off-set (the receptacle is not directly under the squatting slab) double-vault receptacle in the Indian Sopa Sandas latrine. This type can have flap-traps and/or solar heat collectors.

The long drop latrine in figure 52 is the one traditionally used in Yemen.

A *deep receptacle* is used in final deposit systems. The traditional pit and the off-set pit must be at least 3 metres deep in order not to fill up too fast. The borehole usually goes to a depth of at least 6 metres.

The bottom of the pit must in all cases be well above the highest groundwater table to avoid creating favourable conditions for the breeding of *Culex* mosquitoes or pollution of drinking water supplies.

The traditional pit is the most common form of receptacle. Its advantages and drawbacks were described in section 3.13 under Tanzania. The off-set pit is used in the ROEC type of latrine described

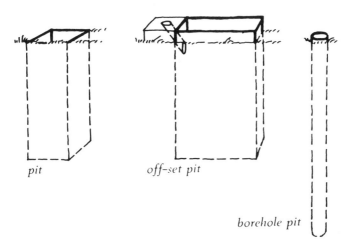

Figure 53   Deep receptacles

in section 3.16 under South Africa. The narrow and deep borehole can only be dug with special equipment.

In its simplest form, the receptacle consists of a hand-dug, unlined hole in the ground. To prevent the edges of the pit from collapsing, you must strengthen them with a frame. This must be put in position before you can dig the pit. You can make the frame of timber as in figure 43, or of reinforced concrete as in figure 106.

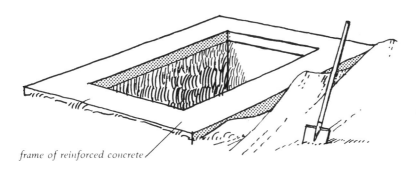

Figure 54   A concrete frame stabilizing the edges of the pit. See also figures 105–106

In unstable soil you have to line the whole pit. Lining material can be bamboo, timber, stones or bricks. If the lining reaches all the way down, the lower half must have open joints or some other arrangement so that liquids can enter the soil.

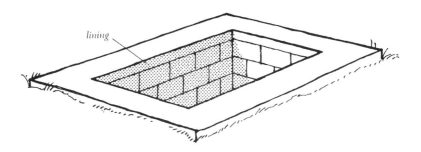

Figure 55   A pit lined with concrete blocks

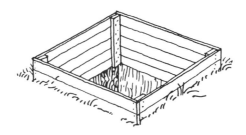

Figure 56   A pit lined with wooden boards

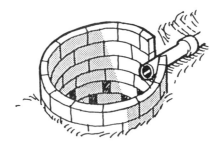

Figure 57   A round pit lined with concrete blocks or bricks. Notice the openings
            that allow seepage of liquid into the surrounding soil

If concrete blocks are made they need not, for a shallow receptacle, be more than 50 millimetres thick. Sixty blocks 50 × 190 × 390 millimetres can be made out of one 50 kilogram bag of cement.

Figure 58   Making concrete blocks

If a deep receptacle is to be lined, it is necessary to use blocks with a thickness of 100–150 millimetres.

A concrete floor is not necessary if the receptacle is placed in a pit. Some polluted liquid may leak into the soil. However, pathogenic organisms do not usually travel through more than a few metres of soil. If the receptacle is on or above the ground surface or the soil conditions are such that groundwater pollution is possible, then it is best to have a concrete floor. This then means that too much liquid must not go into the receptacle. It is best to take away the urine (see under Vietnam and Guatemala in sections 3.3 and 3.4). Another possibility is to fit the receptacle with a solar heat collector to increase the evaporation of liquids.

6.2   Squatting slab

The squatting slab can be either on top of the receptacle or outside it. In the first case the size and shape of the slab depends on the receptacle.

The slab must have a hole, large enough to take faeces and urine without the edges getting soiled, small enough for children not to fall in.

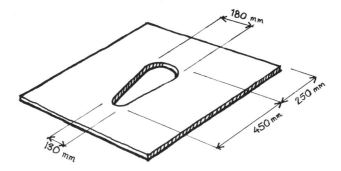

Figure 59   A squatting slab with location and dimensions of the hole. Dimensions
are in millimetres

The slab must have a hard, smooth, easy-to-clean surface. A suitable
material is ferrocement: a rich cement mortar reinforced with chicken
wire. Reinforced concrete is commonly used, but such a slab is much
too heavy for one man to carry and costs more. A ferrocement slab
0.9 × 0.9 metre (or if circular, with a diameter of about 1.0 metre)
need not be more than 18 millimetres thick and weighs about 35
kilograms. In chapter 9 there is a detailed description of how to make
a ferrocement slab (page 122).

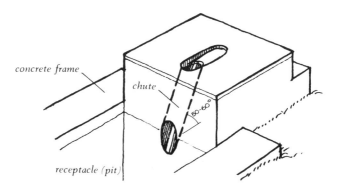

Figure 60   A chute from squatting slab to pit is used in the ROEC latrine and
the Sopa Sandas latrine

The slab can be made from timber and earth as shown in figure 36. This is the most common construction in rural areas. The trouble with such a platform is that the soil surface cannot be properly cleaned and may turn into a breeding ground for parasites like hookworms. The timber support is often attacked by termites.

If the squatting slab is placed off-set from the receptacle, a chute is necessary. It can be made out of a piece of drainpipe or directly from ferrocement. We recommend a diameter of 150 millimetres and a slope of 50–60° for the chute (figure 60).

A squatting slab with a chute has some good points: the user cannot see the contents of the receptacle, and the chute can easily be fitted with a self-closing lid, as shown in figure 24. Experience shows that the chute, if smooth, needs very little cleaning.

6.3   Shelter

The purpose of the shelter is to provide privacy and protection for the user and to stop sunlight and rainwater entering the receptacle.

Figure 61   A shelter of concrete blocks with roof of corrugated-iron sheets

The last point is specially important for compost latrines as they must be kept dry. The shelter should therefore be well constructed and have a proper roof. You can use traditional house building materials or thin building blocks (Gibbs 1984).

A clever design is the spiral-shaped shelter of the VIP latrine. The shape gives privacy without a door and enough darkness for the ventpipe and fly trap to work. The rounded shape gives added strength and helps in the cleaning of the squatting slab.

Not every household accepts the idea of a latrine without a door, though. Many villagers want to be able to lock the latrine. In a survey carried out in Botswana, 80% of the villagers taking part in a sanitation project stated that it is essential for a toilet to have a door (du Pradal 1982). The villagers gave reasons such as 'to prevent fouling by strangers', 'for privacy', 'to keep snakes and animals out' and 'to prevent strangers putting peculiar things into the latrine' (apparently a fear of sorcery).

Figure 62   A spiral-shaped shelter built of mud and wattle

For many people the latrine shelter is a status symbol. They are therefore ready to spend more on the construction of the shelter than is strictly needed for its main purpose: to provide privacy, darkness and protection from rain.

6.4 Aerator

The purpose of an aerator is to bring oxygen from the air into the middle of the pile in a compost latrine.

You can do this in a number of ways: by turning the pile, by bringing air conduits through it (see section 3.2, China), by adding large amounts of grass and straw and by growing earthworms in the latrine.

For a household-sized compost latrine, turning is not necessary. Nor are air conduits necessary. Most important is to add grass and straw to stop the compost pile turning compact and soggy.

Turning, however, helps speed up the decomposition process. You can make a simple turning device from a length of galvanized pipe and a few pieces of reinforcement bars. Figure 63 shows the arrangement.

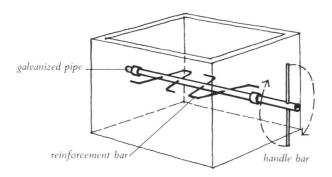

Figure 63   An aerator for a compost latrine

Half a turn two or three times a week is enough if the pile has the right moisture content. If the contents are wet you must turn once a day.

6.5   Baffle

Most compost latrines have two squatting holes or a seat with two holes. If you use a baffle you need only one hole above the partition dividing the receptacle into two chambers.

The baffle directs the latrine input (excreta and refuse) to one of the chambers. When that chamber is full, you turn the baffle plate with a handle. The input then falls into the other chamber.

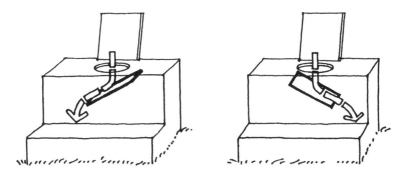

Figure 64   A baffle fitted inside a raised seat

You can fit a latrine without seat with a baffle if you raise the squatting slab about 0.25 metre.

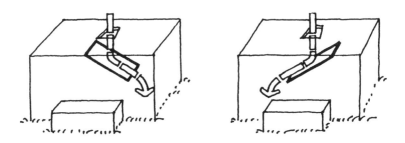

Figure 65   A baffle fitted under a raised squatting slab

6.6   Fly trap

See appendix 2.

6.7 Footrests

The main purpose of the footrests is to guide the latrine user in aiming right, particularly at night.

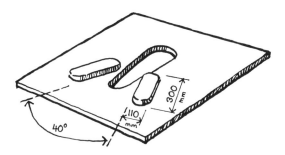

Figure 66   A squatting slab with location and dimensions of footrests. Dimensions are in millimetres

6.8 Handle

A handle on the door (or fixed to the wall of a doorless latrine) is a great help to those who have difficulty getting up from a squatting position.

Figure 67   A handle (see also figure 51)

6.9   Lid

The main purpose of a lid is to stop insects and rodents moving into and out of the receptacle. You can make a lid of wood (see figure 68).

Figure 68   A lid for the squat hole

Double-vault latrines must have two lids. The one covering the vault in use should be made of wood according to the picture above. The lid for the other hole must be heavy and difficult to remove to prevent the use of both vaults at the same time.

stone

Figure 69   A lid for the squat hole not in use (double-vault latrines only)

Another solution is to have movable squatting slabs, one with a hole, the other one without. This arrangement makes sure that only one receptacle at a time can be used.

Should you put hinges on the lid? The underside of the lid often gets slimy. It is not nice to lean your back against. Thus it is best to take away the lid when you sit down. For this reason it is best not to have a lid with hinges. On the other hand, a lid with hinges is more likely to be put back in the right place.

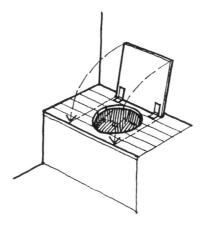

Figure 70   A hinged lid

The problem can in some cases be solved with a self-closing lid. This is not so easy to fix unless the latrine has a chute. The lower end of the chute can have a flap-trap consisting of a piece of tin suspended on two hooks (use non-corroding metal). Occasionally some dirt may stop the tin flap closing completely but like the chute it is self-cleaning. The device has been tested on some latrines in Tanzania and works very well indeed.

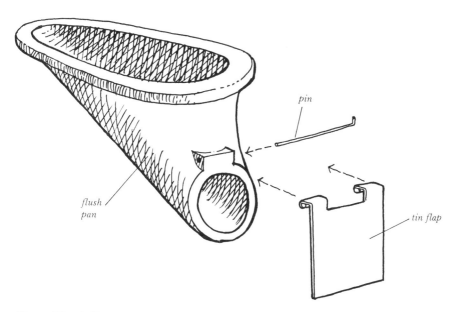

pin

flush
pan

tin flap

Figure 71   A flap-trap

At the Nancy Fulwood Hospital in Sahiwal, Pakistan, Dr Jaap Bouman has developed a chute and flap-trap unit to be bolted to the squatting slab (see figures 72–74). (The chute, if slightly modified, can instead be cast in one piece with the squatting slab (see figure 85).)

Dr Bouman made the chutes in concrete with hinges of 4 millimetres diameter copper wire and flaps of 1.5 millimetre thick bakelite. His report confirms our own findings in Tanzania that the chute is self-cleaning.

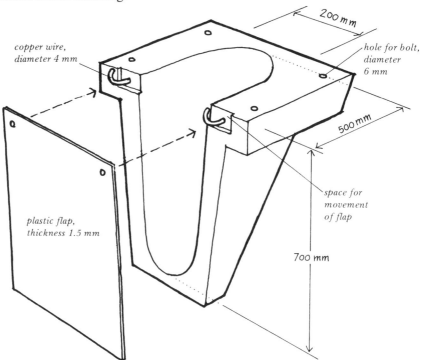

Figure 72   A chute with flap-trap. Dimensions are in millimetres

Figure 73   The chute bolted to a squatting slab, seen here from above

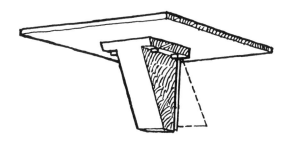

Figure 74   As in figure 73 but seen from below

6.10   Seat

A raised seat is probably more convenient than a squatting slab but is neither healthful nor hygienic. 'The high toilet seat may prevent complete evacuation. The natural position for defecation. . . is the squatting position. . . When the thighs are pressed against the abdominal muscles in this position, the pressure within the abdomen is greatly increased, so that the rectum is more completely emptied' (Kern 1970).

If for cultural reasons a squatting slab is not acceptable, you can add a seat to any type of latrine. The raised seat can be made of wood or of plastic.

In cultures where water is used for anal cleaning, seats must not be used as the cleaning water inevitably fouls the seat.

6.11   Solar heater

You can increase the temperature inside a receptacle if you design it and place it in the sun in such a way that parts of it are heated by the sun. The temperature of the surface of the compost heap can be increased that way. The increase will in most cases be small but is important in fly control as discussed in the appendix. The solar heater will also increase the evaporation from the receptacle.

The easiest way to get solar heat is to expose the top part of the receptacle to the sun and to turn the cover into a collector. You could, for instance, make the cover from a blackened piece of aluminium sheet or a black-painted ferrocement slab (see figure 75).

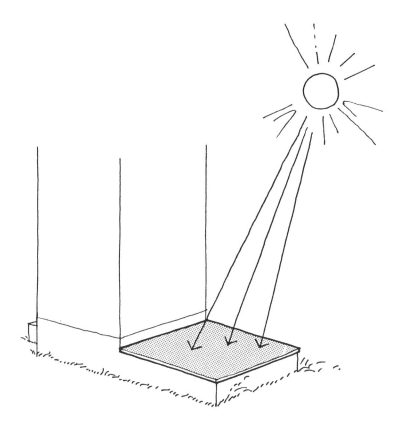

Figure 75   A simple solar heater for the receptacle

6.12   Urine collector

You can design a latrine in such a way that the urine is collected
separately and only the faeces go in the receptacle as shown by
the examples from China, Vietnam, Guatemala and Yemen in chapter
3.

There are three reasons for separating the urine: to keep the
latrine contents dry, to reduce the need for adding high-carbon
material (see section on carbon/nitrogen ratio in chapter 9) and to
conserve the urine's fertilizer value. (The urine, diluted with five
parts of water, you can use in the vegetable garden right away.)

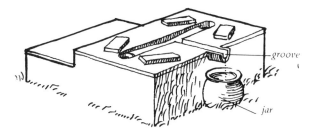

Figure 76   A urine collector. See also figure 8

In some cases we may have to keep urine out of the receptacle although for cultural reasons it cannot be used directly as a fertilizer. Instead of collecting the urine in a jar, we can pipe it into a shallow (0.6 metre) soakpit filled with ashes, husks and dry grass. When the pit no longer absorbs any urine we must cover it with mud and leave it for a couple of months. In the meantime we must use another pit. The decomposed manure from a urine soakpit is an excellent fertilizer.

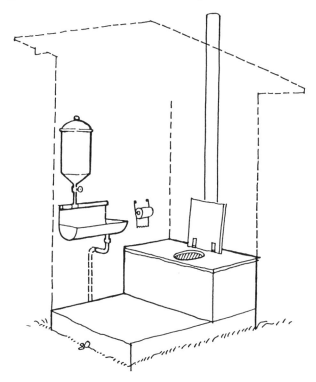

Figure 77   A latrine with separate urinal

6.13　Water-seal trap

The purpose of a water-seal trap is to prevent odour nuisance and fly and mosquito breeding.

A pour-flush latrine can have a forward-facing trap if the squatting slab is right above the receptacle.

A pour-flush latrine must have a rear-facing trap when the squatting slab is connected to the receptacle(s) via a sewer (see figures 86 and 87).

Flush pan with forward-facing trap

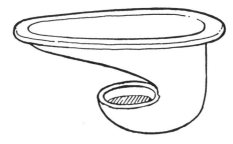

Figure 78　A flush pan with forward-facing trap

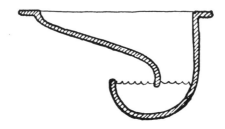

Figure 79　A section through the flush pan shown in figure 78

The following method of making a flush pan with a forward-facing trap has been developed in Chiengmai, Thailand (Wagner and Lanoix 1958).

Make a form in the shape of the inside of the pan. You can make the form of solid wood or of rich cement mortar (two parts cement to one part sand). Put the form upside down on a floor or on the ground (see figure 80).

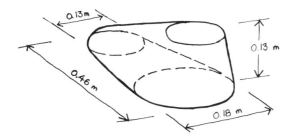

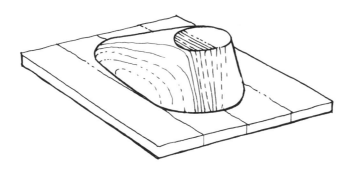

Figure 80   A wooden form for the inside of the pan placed upside down on a floor. The figure above shows the dimensions in metres

Then make the rest of the form of clay. Shape the clay into a roll with a diameter of 80 millimetres. Mould it into a U-shape and place it with one end on a shelf and the other end on the form (see figure 81). The slanting shelf is about 200 millimetres above the base of the form.

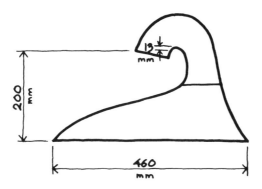

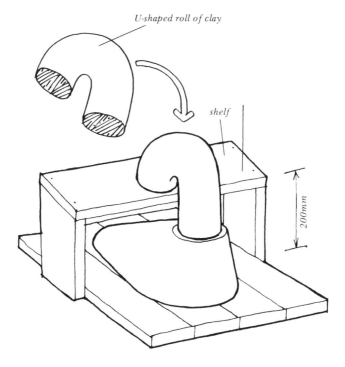

U-shaped roll of clay

shelf

Figure 81   A form for the inside of the water-seal trap is moulded in clay and placed on the wooden form for the pan. A shelf is used to support one end of the U-shaped roll of clay. The other end of the clay roll rests on the form for the pan. The top figure (adapted from Wagner and Lanoix (1958)) shows a section through the flush pan and water-seal trap. Dimensions are in millimetres.

Now smooth the U-shaped clay to the main form (see figure 82). Then oil the whole form.

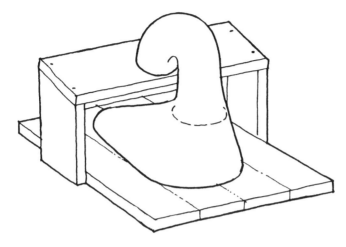

Figure 82 As figure 81 but with the joint between the form for the pan and the form for the trap smoothed with clay

Mix a thin cement–sand slurry and press it over the form by hand. Dust on some dry cement. This treatment will give the pan a dense, smooth interior surface.

Make a stiff mortar of one part cement and three parts sand. Press it on by hand and use a trowel to smooth the mortar to a thickness of 12 millimetres (see figure 83).

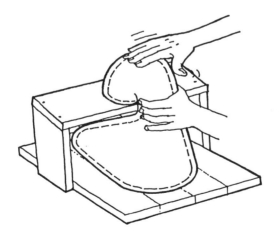

Figure 83 A 12-millimetre-thick layer of mortar applied to the form

Leave the unit in place for 24 hours or longer. Keep it in the shade and cover it with a piece of wet cloth. Then remove the pan from the form together with the clay core. Dig out the clay as in figure 84.

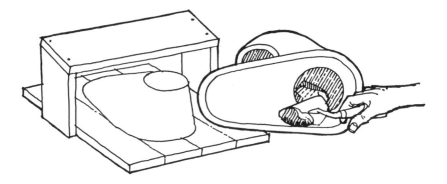

Figure 84   The U-shaped clay core of the trap removed with a spoon or a trowel

Wash the whole pan/water seal with a cement–water slurry. Put the finished unit aside and keep it in the shade for one week. (With one 50 kilogram bag of cement you can make 25–30 units.)

When the pan/water seal unit has cured for a week, put it upside down in a form for the squatting slab (see figure 85). Make the squatting slab of ferrocement as described on page 122.

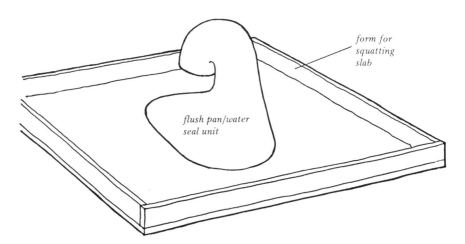

*form for
squatting
slab*

*flush pan/water
seal unit*

Figure 85   The completed pan/trap unit placed upside down in a form to be cast into one piece with the squatting slab

Flush pan with rear-facing trap

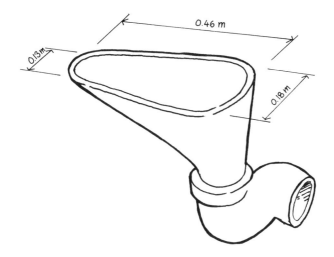

Figure 86   A flush pan with rear-facing trap. Dimensions are in metres

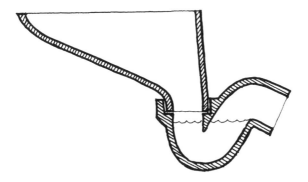

Figure 87   A section through the flush pan in figure 86

The following method for making a rear-facing trap has been developed by the National Environmental Engineering Research Institute (NEERI) in Nagpur, India (Handa 1975).

Make an inner form in the shape of the inside of the pan. Make an outer form in two parts following the shape of the outside of the pan.

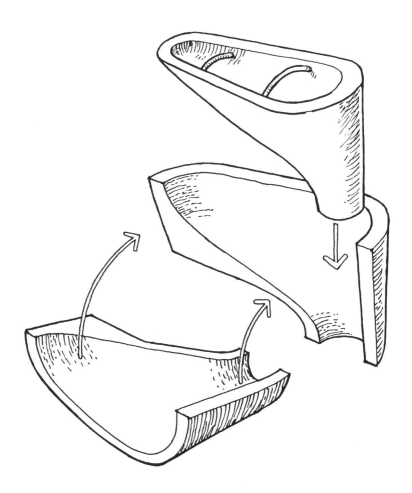

Figure 88   Inner and outer forms for casting the pan

The gap between the inner and the outer forms should be the same as the thickness of the pan, 6 millimetres. The forms can be moulded of rich cement mortar (two parts cement to one part sand).

Let the forms dry in the shade for a few days. Keep them covered with wet sacks. Oil the forms before you cast the pan so that forms and pan can be easily separated.

Put the forms together as shown in figure 89. A metal band around top and bottom will hold the two halves of the outer form together.

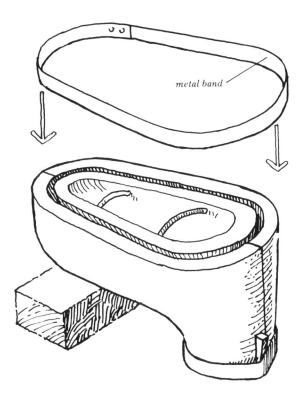

metal band

Figure 89   The forms assembled for casting a pan

Fill the 6 millimetre wide space between the inner and the outer forms with a stiff mortar made of one part cement and three parts of sand (see figure 90).

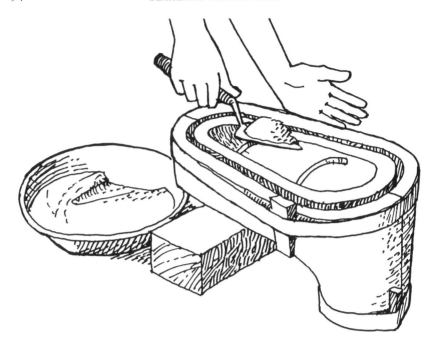

Figure 90   Casting the pan

After two hours remove the inner form. Apply a 6 millimetre coating of white mosaic. This consists of equal parts of white cement, filler (soapstone powder) and mosaic (small chips of marble). An alternative is to give the pan a coating of a white cement slurry. This will give the pan a dense, smooth interior surface.

Leave the pan in the form for 24 hours. Keep it in the shade for two days. Finally, smooth the surface of the pan with a carborundum stone.

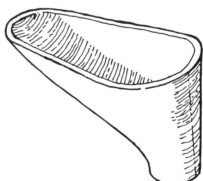

Figure 91   A pan when taken out of the form

The trap is made in a similar way but without the white mosaic (it is enough to coat the inner surface with a cement slurry). Use a mortar made of one part of cement and two parts of sand. The trap has to be made in two halves (see figure 92).

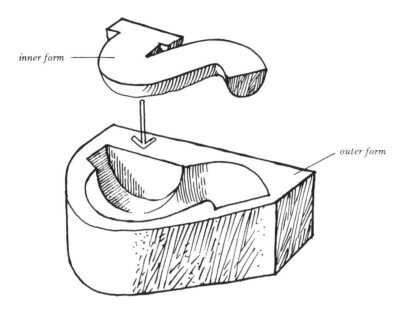

Figure 92   Casting the trap

Take out the trap after 24 hours and join the two halves (see figure 93).

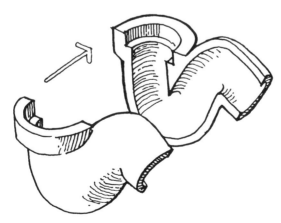

Figure 93   Joining the two halves of the trap

The pan and the trap are assembled as in figure 86. Pan and trap are then built into a platform as in figure 97.

A skilled mason can make at least four pans and four traps every day (provided he has enough forms). An unskilled worker could during the same time smooth six pans.

6.14   Ventpipe

A ventpipe is not necessary but it improves the latrine in two important ways: odours are ventilated away and filth flies are trapped. The ventpipe can be made of bamboo, mud and wattle, ant-hill soil, ferrocement, masonry or plastic. (Ventpipes must not be made of any material likely to rust. Not even galvanized steel should be used.)

Recent fieldwork in Botswana and Zimbabwe (Ryan and Mara 1983) has shown that the main factors responsible for the updraught in a ventpipe are wind speed and direction. The minimum diameter of the ventpipe for satisfactory odour control is according to these studies:

> pipes of asbestos cement or plastic (PVC) — 100 millimetres;
> pipes of mud and wattle, ferrocement, etc. — 200 millimetres.

A ventpipe of building blocks or bricks should have an internal size of at least 180 × 180 millimetres.

The ventpipe should go at least 0.5 metre above the highest point of the roof. For conically shaped roofs, it is enough to take the pipe to the highest point.

In crowded urban areas and where there is little wind it is desirable to increase the diameter and/or height of the ventpipe.

You must screen the pipe on top to stop insects getting into and out of the receptacle that way. The openings in the mesh must not be more than 1.2 × 1.5 millimetres if they are to control mosquitoes. On the other hand they should not be too small as this will reduce the air flow. The screen must be tough because the fumes from the latrine will wear away many kinds of material. PVC-coated fibreglass screens are effective for at least five years according to experience from Zimbabwe (Ryan and Mara 1983). Ordinary nylon mosquito screens could be used but have to be replaced more often. Screens of stainless steel or copper would be ideal but are usually neither affordable nor available in rural areas.

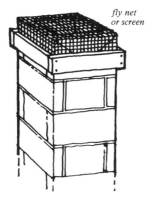

Figure 94   Ventpipe covered with a screen

7 HOW TO BUILD A POUR-FLUSH LATRINE

You can combine the components described in chapter 6 in many ways. The final choice must depend on the local situation. In chapter 3 we presented various pour-flush latrines from India. The one we shall describe here is the double-pit type serving a family of about six people. It consists of receptacle, squatting slab with pan and trap, sewer and shelter.

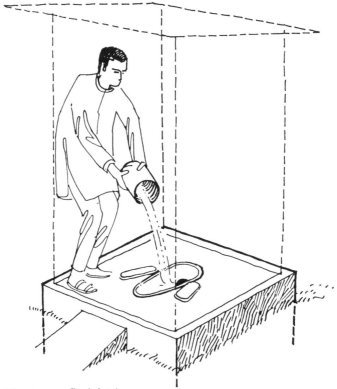

Figure 95   A pour-flush latrine

7.1   Receptacle

Give the receptacle, in this case two pits, a finished internal diameter of 0.9 metre. The depth depends on the permeability of the soil. In sandy soil with good permeability make them a minimum of 1.2 metres deep. In soil with poor permeability make the pits 1.5–2.0 metres deep.

You must line the pits to prevent the walls from caving in. From about 0.3 metre below ground level give the lining openings (open joints or honeycomb brickwork) so that the water can soak into the soil.

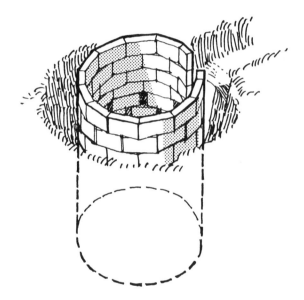

Figure 96   A receptacle. There should preferably be two, see figure 98

7.2   Squatting slab with pan and trap

In areas where pour-flush latrines are common you should be able to buy ready-made pans. The pan can be made of ceramic, fibreglass or concrete. Ceramic and fibreglass pans are smooth and need less water for flushing. A concrete pan is easier to produce locally and therefore costs less. But a concrete surface turns rough and unattractive after some time due to the corrosive effect of urine (India, Technology Advisory Group 1982).

If you are unable to purchase a pan but have cement and the required skills you can make the pan and the trap yourself using the technique described earlier.

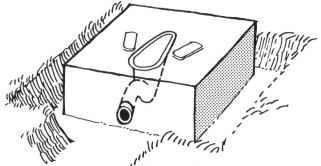

Figure 97   A squatting slab with flush pan and trap

7.3   Sewer

Connect the trap to the pit with 100 millimetre diameter glazed stoneware pipe or PVC pipe.

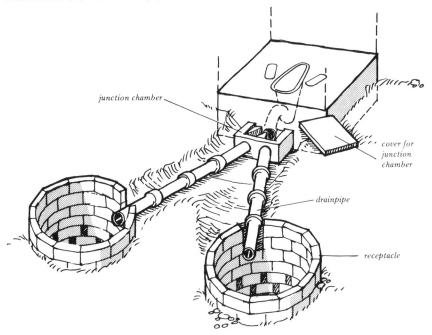

Figure 98   The flush pan with drainpipes from a junction chamber to the receptacles (junction chamber and receptacles are shown without covers)

If such pipes are not available, make the drains of bricks. Round the brick channel into a semi-circular section with cement mortar, or else it might get clogged.

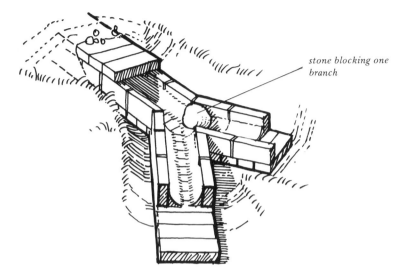

stone blocking one branch

Figure 99   Y-shaped drains built of bricks

In this system, with a pan connected to two pits, give the drains a Y-junction. Block one of the branches with a stone or a brick so that only one receptacle is in use at a time. Figures 99 and 100 show different types of junctions.

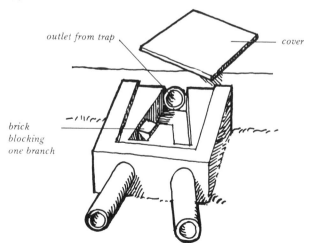

outlet from trap

cover

brick blocking one branch

Figure 100   A junction chamber

To make it easy for you to switch over from one pit to the other, give the Y-junction a tight-fitting cover. Put tight-fitting covers also on the pits.

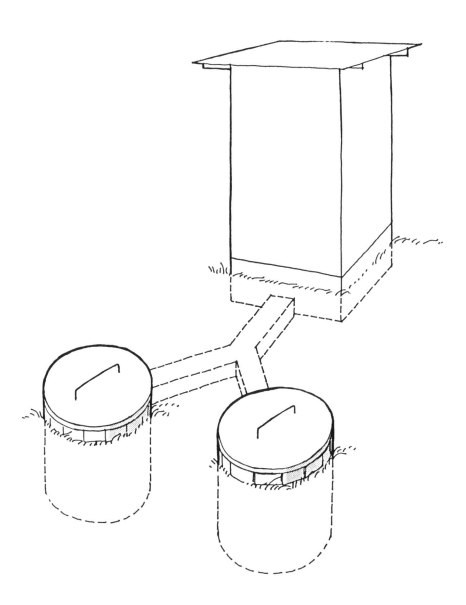

Figure 101   The receptacles covered. The covers must be tight-fitting!

7.4   Shelter

Finally, for privacy and weather protection, build a shelter around the latrine. The shelter of a pour-flush latrine need not be kept dark.

Operation and maintenance instructions are given in chapter 10.

8 HOW TO BUILD A VENTILATED IMPROVED PIT LATRINE

In chapter 3 we presented two types of improved pit latrines: the VIP from Zimbabwe and the ROEC from South Africa. The VIP latrine exists in several versions (see chapter 3). The one we shall describe here is the 'rural VIP latrine'. It consists of receptacle, squatting slab, shelter and ventpipe (Morgan and Mara 1982).

The other ventilated improved pit latrine we describe in this chapter is the 'modified ROEC'.

8.1 The rural VIP latrine

Receptacle

The receptacle is, in this case, a rectangular pit, 0.6 metre wide, 1.5 metres long and at least 3 metres deep.

If the soil is firm, plaster the upper part of the pit wall (down to 1 metre from ground level) with a mortar consisting of one part cement and five parts sand. In less stable soils it may be necessary to line the whole pit (see section 6.1).

Squatting slab

Cover the pit with logs and make a squat hole 200 × 300 millimetres and a ventpipe hole 200 × 200 millimetres as in figure 102.

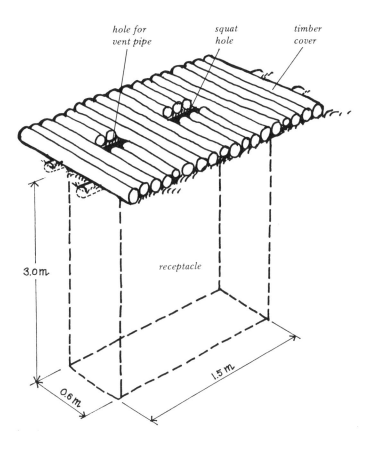

Figure 102   Rural VIP latrine: squatting slab before it is finished with soil (see also figure 36). Dimensions are in metres

Make a smooth floor of soil and/or cement mortar on the part of the squatting slab that will be inside the shelter.

Shelter

The next step is to build the spiral-shaped shelter (see also figure 37 in chapter 3). In Zimbabwe they build the walls of this type of latrine of wooden poles plastered with mud or ant-hill soil. In your case, use a technique based on local building traditions.

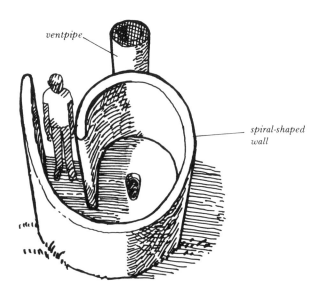

Figure 103   Rural VIP latrine: spiral-shaped shelter seen from above with the roof taken away

Ventpipe

Make a ventpipe of reed mats and cement mortar (one part cement and six parts sand). Make the internal diameter 0.2–0.3 metre (see figure 104). Other ventpipe designs are described at the end of chapter 6. Fix a fly screen to the top of the ventpipe.

Finishing

After you have built the shelter, cover the timber of the squatting slab outside the shelter with soil. Make a mound of rammed earth around the shelter as in figure 44. Plant grass.

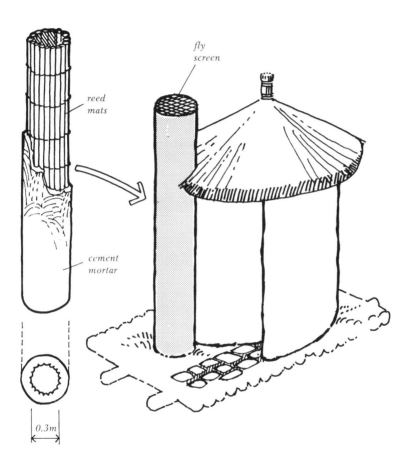

Figure 104   Rural VIP latrine: ventpipe. Dimensions are in metres

Operation and maintenance

Instructions are given in chapter 10.

8.2   The modified ROEC

The second of the ventilated improved pit latrines we describe here takes up quite a lot of space on the ground: you need an area of about 2 × 3 metres. Start by marking out the exact location of the receptacle, 1.0 × 2.0 metres.

Before digging the pit, make a frame around it as shown in figures 105 and 106.

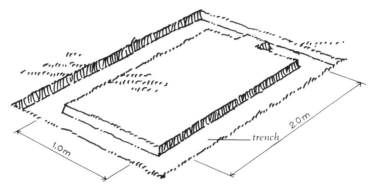

Figure 105   ROEC latrine: trenches for the frame around the pit. Dimensions are in metres

Mix some concrete and cover the bottom of the shallow trench with a layer 20–30 millimetres thick. On top of this place right away two reinforcement bars as shown in figure 106. The reinforcement bars should have a diameter of 8 millimetres or more. Place another layer of concrete, the same thickness as before, on top of the reinforcement.

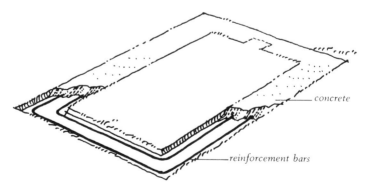

Figure 106   ROEC latrine: casting the frame

If reinforcement bars are not available, the frame can be made from timber as in figure 43.

When the frame is ready and the concrete has set, after a day or two, start digging the pit inside the concrete frame.

Plaster the walls down to 1 metre from the ground with a mortar consisting of one part cement and five parts sand. In unstable soil, line the whole pit (see figure 55).

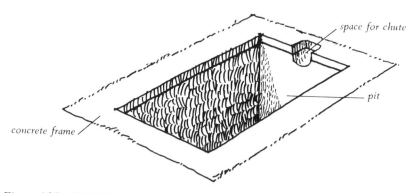

Figure 107   ROEC latrine: digging the pit

You can use any kind of building block for the masonry construction. The concrete blocks in the figures are the 50 × 190 × 390 millimetre blocks we mentioned in section 6.1.

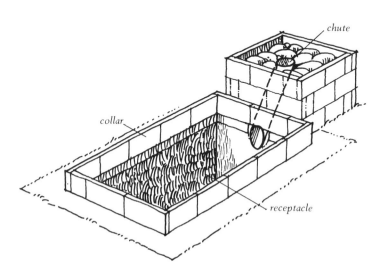

Figure 108   ROEC latrine: foundation

Cast the squatting slab *in situ* and shape it into a bowl around the upper part of the chute. Make a flap-trap for the lower part of the chute (see figure 109 and figure 24).

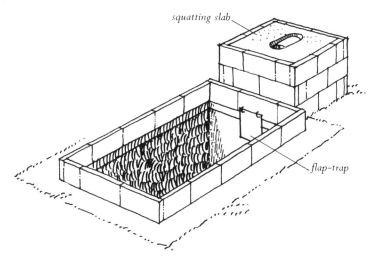

Figure 109   ROEC latrine: squatting slab and flap-trap

You can make the cover over the receptacle from ferrocement as described on page 122. Make it in three sections. Give the one closest to the squatting slab a hole for the ventpipe and a lid-covered manhole so that you can inspect the flap-trap.

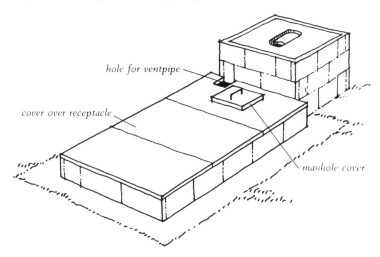

Figure 110   ROEC latrine: covers

Covers and lids must be completely fly-tight. You can do this in several ways: make the covers and lids with a rim, seal all joints with lime mortar, or cover the receptacle with a thick layer of earth. The last method is illustrated in figure 111, which shows the latrine complete with ventpipe and shelter.

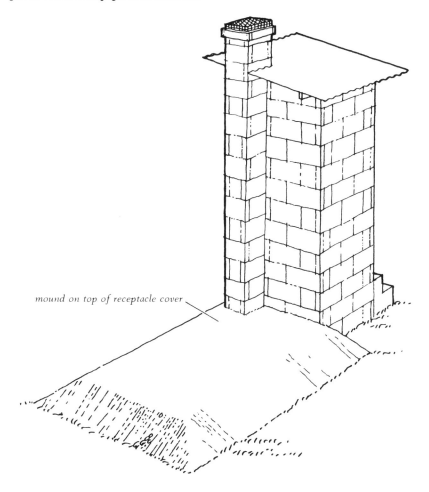

mound on top of receptacle cover

Figure 111   ROEC latrine completed

9 COMPOSTING AND HOW TO BUILD A COMPOST LATRINE

A latrine is a compost latrine only if composting actually occurs in the receptacle. This chapter therefore begins with an outline of the basic principles of composting, life in a compost heap, destruction of pathogenic organisms and the final use of compost.

9.1 Basic principles

Composting is a biological process in which under controlled conditions various types of organisms break down organic substances to make a humus (mature compost). It is the 'controlled conditions' which make the difference between a composting operation and a garbage heap or manure pile.

Ever since life first appeared on earth, organic matter has decomposed by means of biological action. The organisms necessary for decomposition are present in all organic matter.

The art of composting in order to turn human and animal excrement and plant residues into fertilizer was known to many ancient civilizations, notably that of China (see also Gurak *et al*. 1977). In his *Book of Agriculture* written in the 12th century Ibn-al Awam of Seville gives details of how to prepare a compost with human excreta as the major ingredient. The method he used 800 years ago was similar to the one still used in China and described in chapter 3.

The simplest method of composting, in heaps or windrows (elongated heaps) in the open air, is still widely used by gardeners.

Figure 112   A compost heap

The compost builds up gradually: layer upon layer of grass clippings, weeds, all kinds of garden debris and organic household residues form the heap. If you want quicker decomposition you can turn the heap after a week or two and again after a month. Or you can make air channels in the heap as the Chinese often do. However, turning and air channels are not absolutely necessary. You can achieve good results without them (Bruce 1967). Depending on the number of turnings, the season, and the raw material in the heap, the compost may take from four weeks to several months to mature.

Composting is a biological process and is thus influenced by a number of environmental factors such as aeration, temperature, moisture, pH value, and the ratio of carbon to nitrogen (C/N ratio).

Aeration

Some of the microbes need oxygen to carry on the decomposition. Such organisms are said to be aerobic. Others do not require oxygen – they are called anaerobic. Many organisms can be either anaerobic or aerobic depending on the environment. Oxygen is taken from the surrounding air or from air trapped inside the compost heap.

Composting processes are often classified as either aerobic or anaerobic but both types are actually going on at the same time in a compost heap. Near the surface the process may be aerobic while in the interior it is anaerobic.

Aerobic conditions are necessary for rapid, odour-free decomposition and for destruction of pathogenic organisms by heat. Absence of air will lead to different types of micro-organisms developing. Under such conditions decomposition is slower, foul-smelling gases (hydrogen sulphide and ammonia) are released and the heat given off is only a fraction of that from aerobic composting.

The most common way of aerating a compost heap is by turning. A simple device for turning the heap in a compost latrine is described in chapter 6. Another method of aeration is to make air channels right through the heap as shown in the examples from China and Sweden in chapter 3. Earthworms and insects also play an important role in aerating the compost heap. Special aeration devices are therefore usually not necessary especially since only small amounts of oxygen are needed to maintain aerobic conditions.

Temperature

Aerobic decomposition produces a lot of heat. If the heap is large enough, much of the heat is kept, because compost material acts as an insulator. It is possible for the temperature inside a large heap to reach 70°C. But in a compost latrine, the temperature does not usually reach above 50°C. Even this high temperature is only found in a small part of the pile.

Conditions favouring decomposition at higher temperatures are: large bulk (at least 0.5–1.0 cubic metre), low moisture content (50–60%), large input of green grass, weeds and kitchen residues (four or five times the amount of faeces), chopped or crushed raw material, and occasional turning.

Moisture

All organisms need water for life but much moisture in the compost heap may lead to anaerobic conditions. This is because the material becomes soggy, compact and unable to contain sufficient air in the spaces between the particles. A very low content of water on the other hand slows down the activity of the microbes. In a compost latrine we get the best results in terms of pathogen destruction with a moisture content of 50–60%.

An extremely wet latrine could be the result of a combination of some of the following factors: humid climate, water used for anal cleaning, urine as well as faeces gone in, too many users, no addition of organic refuse, unventilated receptacle, entry of rainwater, surface water or groundwater.

The other extreme could result from a dry climate, use of paper or dry leaves for anal cleaning, collection of urine separately and liquid seeping into the subsoil.

Acidity or pH value

Fresh human excreta are slightly acid (pH value less than 7) but after a few days in a compost heap the pH usually begins to rise. Latrine contents are therefore normally alkaline. Highly alkaline conditions will lead to excessive loss of nitrogen in the form of ammonia. You can reduce the amount lost by adding a little soil, about 1% of the weight of the heap, well mixed with the other ingredients. If the process turns anaerobic, large amounts of organic acid are produced, thus lowering the pH. You can increase the pH by adding wood ashes or lime. Normally there is no necessity to influence the pH of a compost latrine.

Ratio of carbon to nitrogen

Microbes feed on organic matter containing, among other things, carbon and nitrogen. They use carbon for energy and nitrogen for body building. The carbon/nitrogen balance in a compost or soil is called the C/N ratio. The microbes need much more carbon than nitrogen: the optimum C/N ratio for composting is thus within the range 15/1 to 30/1 in the initial mixture.

Excreta and especially urine are rich in nitrogen. The C/N ratio of human faeces is around 8/1 and of urine 0.8/1. Green grass clippings and vegetable trimmings have a C/N ratio of about 15/1 while straw and sawdust are very low in nitrogen, with a ratio for straw of about 150/1 and for sawdust up to 500/1. The more the C/N ratio differs from the optimum range of from 15/1 to 30/1, the longer the decomposition takes. To get quick decomposition in a latrine it is therefore necessary to add high-carbon materials like grass, garden

litter, sawdust, and organic household and kitchen residue. Excluding
urine from the latrine (as the Vietnamese do, see chapter 3) has a
similar effect.

9.2   Life in the compost heap

An immense variety of organisms live in and contribute to the break-
down of the compost heap. They range in size from viruses, bacteria,
fungi and algae to earthworms, slugs, arthropods and rodents. It is
this rich fauna and flora that is responsible for the rapid decomposition
in a well functioning compost latrine.

The bigger organisms play a limited role in the decomposition
process in a large composting plant. They are not able to survive the
high temperatures (60–70°C) of a garden compost that is turned
frequently. The conditions in a compost latrine are more favourable
to higher animals as the temperature normally does not exceed
40–45°C.

Fly maggots, earthworms, snails, slugs, ants, mites, spiders, sowbugs,
beetles and cockroaches play a major role in mixing, aerating and
tearing apart the contents of the latrine. As long as they remain inside
the receptacle their activities are good and should be encouraged. It
might even be a good idea to place earthworms in the latrine. If the
environment is favourable for them they will multiply, burrowing
holes through the compost heap, eating odorous organic matter and
thereby converting it into rich organic soil.

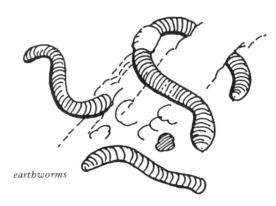

earthworms

Figure 113   Earthworms and other organisms in the compost turn organic
matter into fertile soil

Most of the invertebrate inhabitants of the latrine are harmless to man, but there are some we do not like to see outside: the filth fly, the *Culex* mosquito and the cockroach are obvious examples. Methods for controlling these insects are discussed elsewhere in this book.

Many of the organisms are present in the raw material. However, if you add the partly decomposed material from an existing compost heap to a new heap, this will speed up the process by introducing micro-organisms which are already acclimatized to the heap.

9.3   Destruction of pathogenic organisms

Once the excreta enter a compost latrine they remain there for a long time: from two months up to several years depending on the system used. Sooner or later the latrine must be emptied or closed down. If it is to be emptied: how safe are the contents in terms of the possible spread of disease?

High-temperature composting can effectively destroy pathogenic organisms but, as has been shown previously, high temperatures are not likely in a compost latrine. Temperatures above 50°C, if reached, do not last long, and are likely to be limited to a part of the pile.

High temperature alone is not enough to destroy pathogenic organisms in a latrine. Fortunately other factors in the compost environment help destroy pathogens: time, unfavourable pH value, competition for food, antibiotic action, toxic by-products of decomposing organisms and anaerobic conditions.

After six months in a closed receptacle the contents of a well functioning compost latrine are safe enough to be taken out. Place them in a shallow trench and cover with soil. Most parasitic organisms have been destroyed and the amount of faecal coliform organisms reduced to the level normally found in the soil.

9.4   Compost as a fertilizer and soil conditioner

Compost is vital to the health of growing plants. Its main value is as a soil conditioner, providing whatever may be lacking in the physical and chemical make-up of the soil. This is particularly important for tropical soils which are often low in organic content. Addition of compost will make the soil easier to cultivate and improves its water-holding capacity, thus helping to prevent cracking and erosion by wind and water.

Compost from the Multrum described in chapter 3 has an organic content of 58% (on a dry weight basis). The percentage of major plant nutrients – nitrogen, phosphorus and potassium – can be as high as 2.4%, 3.6% and 3.9% respectively. This means that about 3 kg dry weight (about 10 kg 'wet' weight) is roughly equivalent to 1 kg of '10–10–10' fertilizer. In addition the compost contains significant amounts of the minor plant nutrients calcium, magnesium and sulphur, as well as a variety of trace elements and microbes (Fogel 1977). The major plant nutrients as well as the trace elements are fixed in organic compounds. Therefore in spite of the relatively low percentage of nutrient contents in compost, their use by plants can be close to 100%. Chemical fertilizers, on the other hand, are soluble in water and will, to a large extent, be washed into groundwater, streams and lakes. A high percentage of the nutrients in chemical fertilizers are therefore not used by the plants.

The amount of major plant nutrients ('N–P–K') available to developing countries through organic residues and night soil was in 1971 seven or eight times larger than their actual consumption of manufactured fertilizers (FAO/SIDA 1975). Few countries are systematically making use of this treasure – the notable exceptions being China, Vietnam and, in India, Ladakh.

'Wastes' is obviously a misleading term for excreta, kitchen waste, sweepings, and crop and garden leavings. The rest of the world must learn from the Chinese to regard these residual products as valuable resources. The term 'waste' should be replaced by 'residue'.

9.5 How to build a double-vault compost latrine

In its simplest form a double-vault compost latrine consists of a receptacle divided into two vaults, a squatting slab, a shelter and a ventpipe.

Receptacle

Start by digging a pit approximately 1.5 × 1.8 metres. The pit could be up to 1.0 metre deep depending on the location of the highest groundwater table. In the series of illustrations that follow we have indicated the pit as being 0.5 metre deep. The earth floor of the pit is also the bottom of the receptacle.

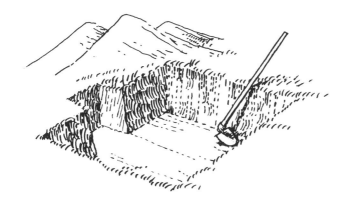

Figure 114   Double-vault compost latrine: digging a hole for the receptacle

If the area where you are building your latrine is waterlogged or seasonally flooded you must not dig a pit but instead place it on a mound. In such a case the receptacle should have a concrete floor as shown below.

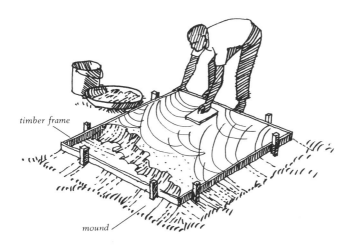

timber frame

mound

Figure 115   Double-vault compost latrine: casting the floor (necessary only when the whole receptacle is above ground)

For the first four layers (0.8 metre) you just take the five walls straight up. The receptacle is divided into two vaults by a partition as shown below.

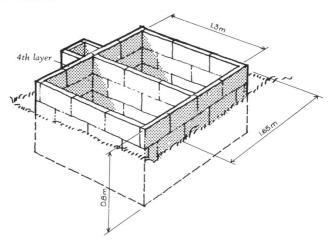

Figure 116   Double-vault compost latrine: the first four layers of concrete blocks. Dimensions are in metres

The fifth layer is laid the same way but here you put some blocks across to provide a beam. Place this beam 0.8 metre from the rear wall. The blocks forming the beam must be supported until the mortar has set. The span is so short that there is no need for any permanent reinforcement.

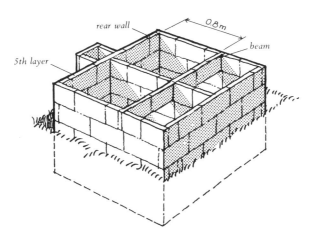

Figure 117   Double-vault compost latrine: the fifth layer. Dimensions are in metres

If you are using 50 millimetre blocks: before you proceed with the sixth layer, put some blocks on the flat side around the front part of the receptacle as shown by the figure below. These blocks provide support for the covers to be added later.

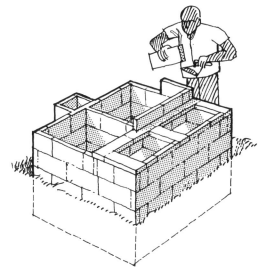

Figure 118   Double-vault compost latrine: support for the covers

The sixth layer is placed only around the part of the receptacle to be covered by the squatting slab. Leave a hole for the ventpipe.

Before you continue the masonry work, place the squatting slabs in position.

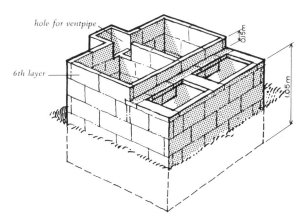

Figure 119   Double-vault compost latrine: the sixth layer. Dimensions are in metres

Squatting slab

It is best to make the squatting slabs and covers from ferrocement. This is a mixture of cement, sand and water reinforced with chicken-wire mesh. Make a form for the squatting slab: internal measurements 0.9 × 0.87 metre and 18 millimetres deep. (The slab need not be more than 18 millimetres thick!) Place three layers of chicken-wire mesh in the form. Cut out the hole, 0.12 × 0.40 metre through the three layers and place a block of wood there. (If wire mesh is not available it is possible to reinforce the slab with sisal fibre or coconut fibre.)

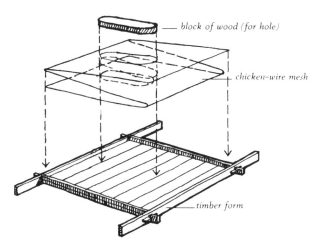

— block of wood (for hole)

— chicken-wire mesh

— timber form

Figure 120   Making a squatting slab of ferrocement

Mix one part cement with two parts sand. For a slab of 0.9 × 0.9 metre and 18 millimetres thick you need 11 kilograms (9.5 litres) cement and 22 kilograms (17.5 litres) sand. Add water until you have a rather stiff mortar (roughly 0.4 parts water by weight). Too much water in the mortar will reduce the strength of the slab.

Apply the mortar with a trowel and force it into the layers of mesh. Press the mortar hard and shake the form by tapping it with a hammer so that no empty spaces will be left inside the slab.

Place the form with the slab in the shade and cover it with wet sacking to prevent the slab from drying out during the cement hardening process. Keep the sacks wet.

After 24 hours the slab can be taken out of the form and the form used again. Put the slab in the shade for a few days and keep it covered with wet sacks.

You can make footrests from cement mortar. If you want to mass-produce slabs, it is better to incorporate the shape of the foot-rests in the form for the slab.

Repeat the process for the second slab and the two covers. Make the covers 0.50 × 0.87 metre and about 18 millimetres thick. It is best to make them with a rim to make it more difficult for flies to escape through the joint between the covers and the receptacle.

Figure 121 shows the squatting slab and the covers in position. Fix the squatting slabs permanently by settling them in mortar. Make the covers removable.

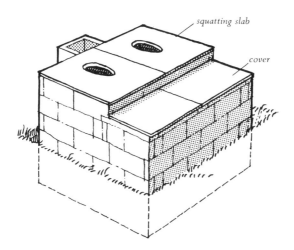

Figure 121   Double-vault compost latrine: squatting slabs and covers

Shelter and ventpipe

Continue the masonry work until the shelter, including the ventpipe, is completed. Add steps, door, roof and, on top of the ventpipe, a mosquito screen.

Put several layers of well tamped earth against the walls of the receptacle so that rainwater is drained away from the latrine.

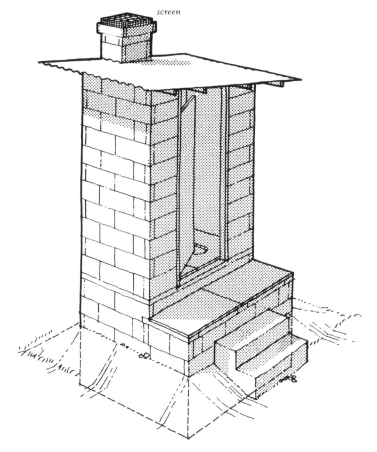

screen

Figure 122   Double-vault compost latrine: completed. Make a mound of
             rammed earth around the latrine (see also figure 44)

9.6   A multi-unit compost latrine

The preliminary version of this book dealt exclusively with latrines
for single households. Many readers have, however, asked for advice
on how to build communal latrines at schools, clinics and similar
institutions in areas where water is too precious to be flushed away
through a WC.

The problem with public or communal facilities is not so much
how to design and build a latrine, but rather how to keep it clean
and how to operate it properly. The ROEC type, for instance, can,
without any alterations, be used as a public latrine.

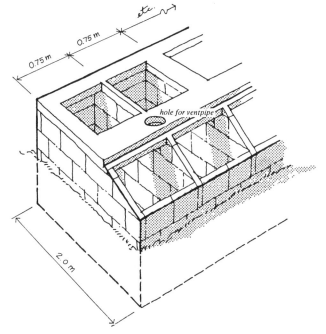

Figure 123   A multi-unit, solar-heated compost latrine: receptacles divided into two vaults. Dimensions are in metres

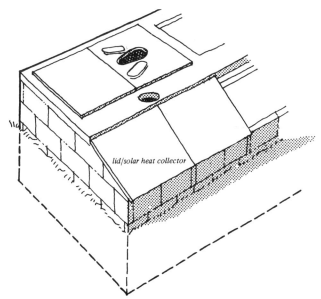

Figure 124   A multi-unit, solar-heated compost latrine: the vault in use is covered with a squatting slab; the other is covered with a slab with no hole. The slabs are changed when the first vault is full

Compost latrines, like any other type, must be cleaned frequently and in addition they need a daily input of organic refuse. Once or twice a year they must be emptied and users have to shift from one chamber to the other. Somebody must be in charge of these operations. If this can be arranged, you can use compost latrines as communal units.

The figures shown here illustrate one suitable combination of components. Four double-vault units have been combined and would probably cater for 40–50 people. (The solar heat collector increases the capacity of the latrine as compared to an ordinary latrine without heating device.)

The ventpipe is essential for fly and odour control. One ventpipe serves two chambers, which means that the latrine illustrated here has four ventpipes.

Figure 125   The multi-unit, solar-heated compost latrine completed

A urinal should be built near the men's latrine. The urine could be collected, diluted and used as a fertilizer or, if this is not possible, drained away in a soakpit. Less urine in the receptacle means less need for organic refuse which in turn would give a longer retention time.

10 OPERATION AND MAINTENANCE

The construction of a latrine is only the first step. Proper use, careful upkeep and adequate disposal of the contents are equally important.

10.1 Instructions for compost and pit latrines

The operating instructions in this section are primarily intended for those who use compost latrines but might as well be followed also by those who have pit latrines. Any pit latrine will function better if it is managed like a compost latrine. It is more likely to remain dry, the decomposition will be quicker, odours and fly and mosquito breeding will be reduced.

Starting up

Before the latrine is used for the first time, fill the receptacle with loosely packed organic residue: grass, weeds, leaves, straw, husks, sawdust, yard sweepings — whatever is available. This absorbs liquid, provides carbon for the decomposition, increases the variety of micro-organisms and prevents the pile from becoming too compact. All compost and pit latrines will function better if you start them up like this.

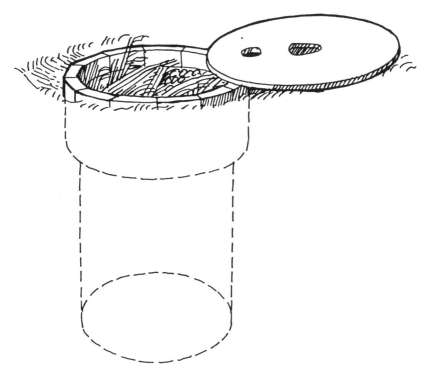

Figure 126   Before a pit latrine or compost latrine is used for the first time, fill it up with grass, weeds, husks, etc.

Utensils and materials

Inside the latrine shelter, make sure there is a brush for sweeping the squatting slab. Do not use this brush for any other purpose. Place a box or a jar full of ashes, husks, sawdust, dry earth or a mixture of such materials in a corner of the latrine shelter. Keep an empty tin or a coconut shell in the box to help in sprinkling of the dry material. If water is used for cleaning the anus, keep a bucket of water in the shelter together with a tin for scooping it up.

Daily use

Relate the number of regular users to the capacity of the latrine. The capacity depends not only on the volume of the receptacle but to a great extent also on what you put into the latrine.

Do not overload a compost latrine! The result will be a soggy mess, very unpleasant to clean out. If the receptacle is the final depository (traditional pit latrine, ventilated pit latrine or ROEC), overuse will drastically reduce the life of the latrine.

Use the latrine for excreting purposes only, not as a bathroom!

Sprinkle ashes, husks or powdered earth after each defecation.

Replace the lid.

When the slab becomes soiled: sprinkle with ashes and sweep into the receptacle. If water is used, use sparingly!

Regular upkeep

Put into the receptacle, preferably every day, all floor and yard sweepings as well as kitchen leftovers.

Figure 127   Put floor and yard sweepings into the latrine

Several times a week put grass clippings, weeds, straw or leaves in the receptacle. Do not worry about filling it up too fast. The volume of whatever organic material you put in will in the end be reduced by 95%.

Figure 128   Put grass and weeds into the latrine

Do not throw glass, tins or plastic into the latrine. Avoid also slowly degradable materials such as corncobs, sugar canes, mango kernels and wooden sticks.

Save up the ashes and put them in the box mentioned previously, for later use in the latrine. The ashes deodorize the excreta, make the faecal matter less attractive to flies and absorb moisture.

Figure 129   Put ashes into the latrine

Save all husks and use them for sprinkling if there are not enough ashes for this purpose. If not needed for sprinkling, you can dump them directly into the receptacle.

Figure 130   Put husks into the latrine

If there is a bucket of water for anal cleaning, make sure that the bucket is cleaned and emptied regularly, at least once every week, to prevent mosquitoes from breeding in it.

Changing vaults

When the receptacle of a compost latrine is filled to within 0.3–0.4 metre from the slab it is time to switch over to the other vault. (In the case of a pit latrine a new pit has to be dug and the squatting slab shifted to the new position.)

Cover the pile in the compost latrine with grass and top up with soil. Close the vault with a heavy lid – either a special lid made of concrete or a piece of wood with a stone on top. The purpose of the heavy lid is to prevent any further use of this vault until the compost has been removed. Prepare the second receptacle as described under 'Starting up' earlier in this chapter.

Removing compost

When the second receptacle is nearly full it is time to remove the compost from the first one. Take off the cover and scoop up the contents with a hoe. Do not remove all of it – leave some to give the new pile a good start.

Figure 131   Double-vault compost latrine: removing the compost

The compost should by now be fairly dry, soil-like and completely odour-free. It is certainly not sterile but should be no more dangerous to handle than the soil in the garden.

Carry the compost to the vegetable plot or nearest field and put it in a shallow trench.

Figure 132   Put the compost in a shallow trench in the garden

Cover it with about 0.1 metre of soil and grow vegetables on top.

10.2   Instructions for pour-flush latrines

The most important instruction for flush latrines is that you must use water or toilet paper for anal cleaning. Any other material will clog the water seal and the drainpipe.

Starting up

If you have a double-pit pour-flush latrine, you must block one of the drains at the Y-junction. Flush excreta into one of the pits only.

Before the latrine is used for the first time make sure that sewer, Y-junction and receptacle are properly sealed. If not, the receptacle will turn into a breeding ground for mosquitoes and flies.

Utensils and materials

Make sure that inside the latrine shelter there is a brush for cleaning the pan. Never use this brush for any other purpose.

Place a bucket of water inside the latrine shelter. Use this water for anal cleaning and flushing.

Daily use

Wet the pan before every use by pouring some water into it. The water will act as a lubricant and prevent excreta from sticking to the pan.

Flush the pan properly after each use (2–3 litres of water). Do not use more water than is necessary.

Do not use the latrine enclosure for bathing or for washing clothes. This would put a heavy load on the pit. It might cause it to overflow, spreading fresh excreta, causing nuisance as well as a health hazard.

Regular upkeep

Once a week flush the pan with a bucketful of water to prevent build-up of excreta in the trap and the sewer.

Changing receptacles

When the first pit is full, open the drain leading to the second pit. Close the drain leading to the full pit.

After some years, when the second pit is full, the first pit contains only a small amount of humus. It is a valuable fertilizer. Take care of it as described under 'Removing compost' above. Then open the drain leading to the now empty pit and block the other one.

10.3   Maintenance

A 'maintenance-free' disposal system does not exist. The simple, self-built latrines described in this book may require a great deal of maintenance. But they all have the advantage that the users themselves can repair them. They are simple enough to require only the skills and materials readily available in the community.

Two things are specially important: keep out surface water and make sure the receptacle is fly-tight.

Arrange the ground around the latrine so that surface water drains away from the receptacle. Soil erosion may change the direction of the flow. Check this during the rainy season.

Screen openings, repair holes and cracks and check that lids and covers are tight-fitting. A fly needs but a tiny crack to escape from the receptacle.

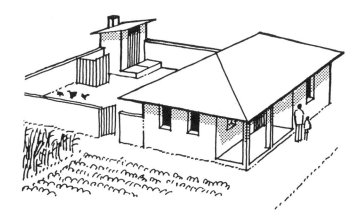

Figure 133

APPENDIX 1

How to build a soakpit and a bath

In many cases you can use water from kitchen, bath and laundry to irrigate the kitchen garden and to water domestic animals. If there is still a surplus of water to be disposed of, do not allow it to flow into the latrine. Nor must it form pools of stagnant water around house, standpost or handpump.

Direct waste water into a soakpit. In its simplest form, this is a hole in the ground filled with stones, broken bricks or coconut shells. But silt, grease and microbiological activities will soon clog the pit.

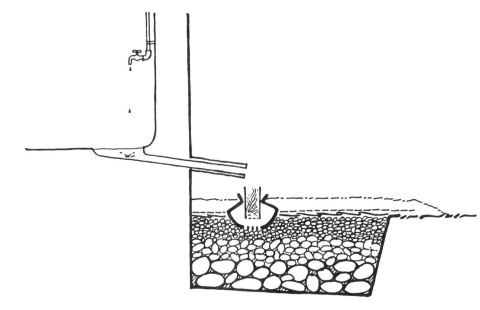

Figure 134   Section through soakpit

It smells and flies and mosquitoes breed there. The useful life of such a pit is likely to be less than a year.

A properly built soakpit should last for many years. A condition is that it has a silt and grease trap. For a daily flow of not more than 200–300 litres the pit should be about 1 metre wide, 1 metre long and 0.7–0.8 metre deep (Patel 1970).

Fill up one-third of the pit with big, round stones the size of a papaya or coconut. Continue with stones the size of a mango up to about 0.3 metre from the ground surface.

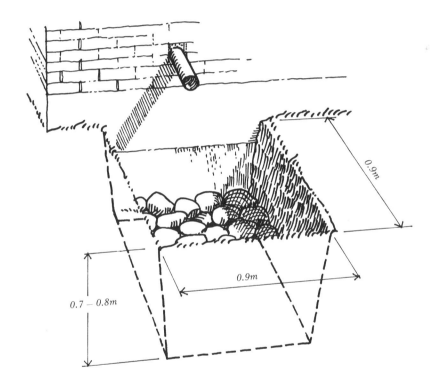

Figure 135   Soakpit: first put a layer of coconut-sized stones into the pit. Dimensions are in metres

Make a silt and grease trap: Take an earthenware pot with a wide mouth and make little holes through the bottom of it. Take a tin can small enough to fit into the pot and punch holes through the bottom as shown in figure 137. Place a layer of coconut bark (or similar fibrous material) into the pot, place the tin in the pot and put some of the same material or grass into the tin.

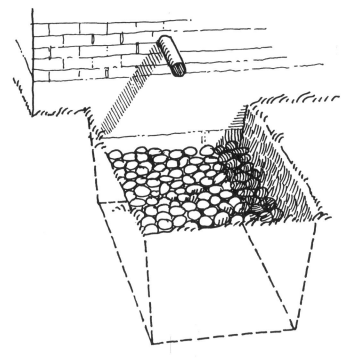

Figure 136   Soakpit: add a second layer of smaller (mango-sized) stones

Figure 137   Silt and grease trap: make holes in an earthenware pot and a tin can

Figure 138   Silt and grease trap: put some fibrous material into the pot and into the tin

Figure 139   Soakpit: place the silt and grease trap in the pit and fill up with pebbles. If you have some charcoal, include a layer of it here

The silt and grease trap should be placed into the pit, and the pit filled up with pebbles. If charcoal is available, a layer of it should be included on top of the pebbles. Then cover the pit with palm leaves and sack cloth.

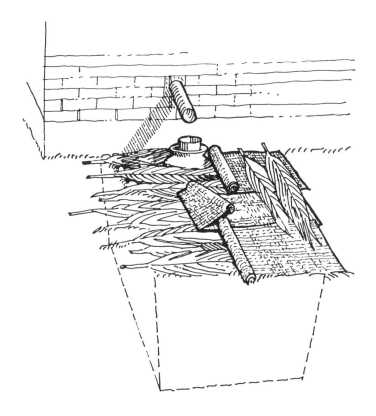

Figure 140   Soakpit: cover the pebbles with a 50 millimetre layer of palm leaves, a layer of gunny (sack) cloth and then another 50 millimetre layer of palm leaves

Finally cover the pit with a 50–80 millimetres thick layer of mud.

Solid particles and grease in the waste water will be caught in the silt and grease trap. Change the grass and the coconut bark in the trap

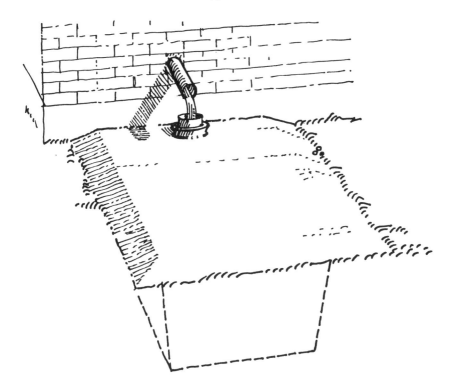

Figure 141   Soakpit completed

every second week. If you do this regularly the soakpit will last five, maybe ten, years.

When the pit is no longer soaking water it must be opened and cleaned. Take out the stones and pebbles and rinse them. Take away a layer of 100 millimetres of soil from all the walls. Let the pit dry in the sun for some days and then rebuild it as described above.

Every household should have not only a latrine but also a bathroom. If there is not a separate enclosure, there is a risk that people will use the latrine not only for defecation and anal cleaning, but also for ablution. A compost latrine turns into a stinking cesspool if large amounts of water are poured into the receptacle. You must also keep pit latrines dry to avoid mosquito breeding.

Figure 142 shows a latrine with bath enclosure attached. Water from the bath drains into a proper soakpit.

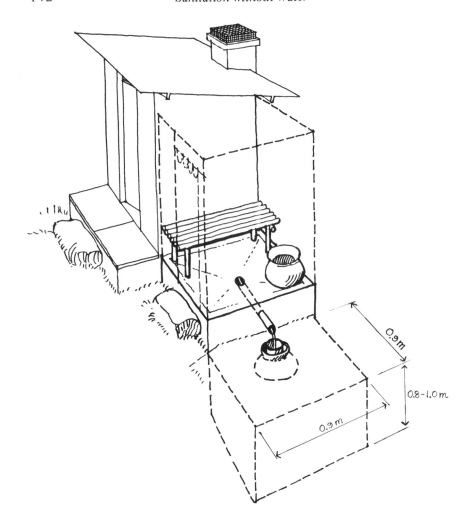

Figure 142   A latrine with bath and soakpit. Dimensions are in metres

APPENDIX 2

Fly and mosquito control

When you introduce latrines in an area, you are likely to get many more flies and mosquitoes. Latrines make an excellent breeding ground for various types of filth flies. If the contents of the receptacle are wet, the risk is great that *Culex* mosquitoes will also breed there. From one latrine alone more than 1000 adult mosquitoes may emerge every day.

The adult fly can transmit infectious organisms in a number of ways: by the sticky hairs of its feet, by the hairs of its body, by regurgitation of its vomit drops and by its faeces. Diseases that can be transmitted by these flies include typhoid fever, the paratyphoids, cholera, bacillary dysentery, infantile diarrhoea, trachoma, poliomyelitis, yaws, amoebic dysentery and giardiasis. Certain worms can also be transmitted by flies (West 1951).

The *Culex* mosquito is an important vector of Bancroftian filariasis and certain viruses in parts of the tropics (see chapter 2) and is the major nuisance mosquito in tropical urban areas.

In this appendix we shall describe and comment on a number of methods of fly and mosquito control and point out which ones can be used for the types of latrines we are recommending. The various control measures have been grouped under the four headings 'mechanical', 'thermal', 'chemical', and 'biological'.

Mechanical control

The best method of controlling mosquito breeding in latrines is to build and use the latrines in such a way that they do not get wet. A latrine must therefore not reach down into the groundwater, and it must be protected from surface water. In addition you must not

143

pour any water except that used for anal cleaning into the receptacle. Even with these precautions there is a risk that the contents of a latrine may turn liquid enough to attract egg-laying mosquitoes. You must therefore add dry materials like sawdust, ash, lime, husks, floor sweepings and powdered earth to the latrine every week.

Other methods against mosquito breeding include pouring oil over the surface of the water in the latrine, or covering the wet surface with a layer of expanded polystyrene balls (Reiter 1978).

Filth flies may be attracted to a latrine even if it is too dry for mosquito breeding. For effective fly control, you must add even more dry matter, preferably after every use. Flies do not lay eggs in any material with a moisture content of less than 65%.

Some experts suggest keeping the receptacle dark as a way of controlling flies. This is a good idea because flies are attracted by light. But it is not enough. Flies do breed in dark pit latrines, in borehole types as well as in ROEC units, although both are supposedly 'fly-proof'.

Professor Jettmar (1940) claimed that 'it is mere superstition that latrine flies do not breed in dark borehole latrines'.

Many latrines have a lid over the squat hole. As a control measure it is not very efficient. Flies and mosquitoes do get in while the latrine is being used. In many cases the lid is not put back properly. Some of the kitchen residues put in the compost latrine may already be flyblown. A self-closing device like the flap-trap described in chapter 6 is likely to be more effective than a hand-operated lid.

Some people suggest screening the latrine building but the effect is doubtful as in practice it is almost impossible to have it done and maintained properly. Besides, it does not work well for compost latrines for reasons mentioned above.

A screened ventpipe acts as a fly and mosquito trap if properly designed, see section 3.14. This kind of trap is self-cleaning and will automatically deposit the dead insects into the pit.

Experiments with traps fitted on ventpipes caught about 80% of the mosquitoes and over 90% of the flies attempting to leave the pit and also prevented egg-carrying mosquitoes from entering (Curtis and Hawkins 1982). A trap in the drop hole would further reduce the number entering or leaving the receptacle.

If you want to use the dead flies as chicken feed you can make a trap from an empty paint or kerosene tin and a piece of mosquito net as in figures 143 and 144. The trap has to be emptied frequently — maybe twice a week in the fly season. (Cover the hole while you are emptying the trap!)

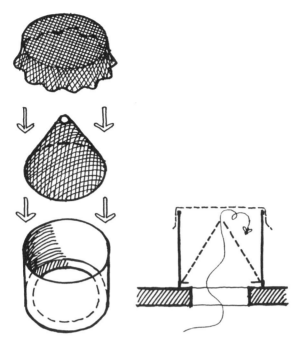

Figure 143   A latrine-attached fly trap made from an empty paint tin

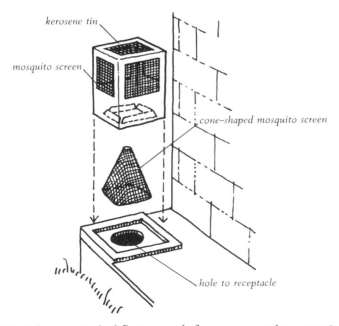

Figure 144   A latrine-attached fly trap made from an empty kerosene tin

Near the latrine you can use free-standing fly traps made from kerosene tins as above or from timber and mosquito net as in figure 145. A free-standing trap must be baited. Use animal intestines, manure or, best of all, yeast. Mix yeast with water, allow mixture to stand 3–4 days with loosely sealed lid. Renew the bait after 3–5 days (Satrom and Stephens 1979).

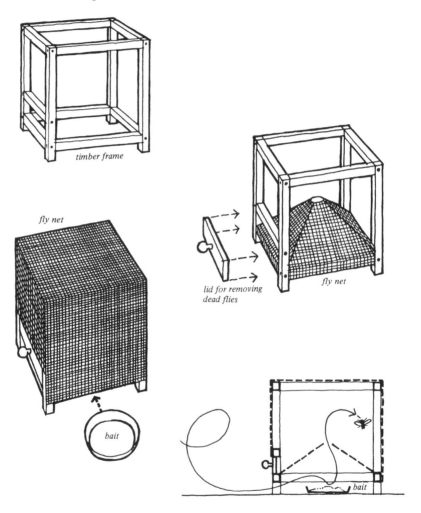

Figure 145   A free-standing fly trap with bait

Fly swatters are useful tools in fly control inside houses, especially in combination with screening.

Thermal control

In a latrine flies cannot easily be killed by high temperatures. The temperatures in a latrine receptacle are usually too low. If the temperature inside the pile rises above 49°C (the lethal temperature for adult flies), the surface temperatures may still be low enough for maggots to survive. They are in any case able to move to cooler parts of the receptacle. The eggs are more sensitive – they cannot move and are more sensitive to high temperatures than larvae and pupae. Eggs will hatch at 40°C, some will survive at 41°C, but none at 43°C. The exact lethal temperature depends also on the duration of the exposure (West 1951).

Temperature on the surface of the pile in a compost latrine can be increased by solar heating of the receptacle as described in chapter 6. In most of the tropics it should be possible, with quite simple arrangements, to increase pile surface temperature to 43°C or above.

Daily burning is a useful control measure for military latrines. Hay or straw is thrown into the pit, a sprinkling of crude oil added and the whole pile set on fire. Outside a military establishment the method might be used for temporary latrines, for instance, in refugee camps. We cannot recommend the method for permanent latrines and household size units as it is difficult to ensure that the burning is carried out regularly. Besides, not only flies but also many useful organisms would be destroyed by the fire.

Like flies, adult mosquitoes would also die of heat if you burned hay or straw inside the receptacle. A water temperature of 40°C would kill the aquatic stages of the mosquito or cause a high rate of abnormality in the emerging adults. Solar heating of the receptacle might therefore be useful also in mosquito control. A solar-heated latrine is more likely to remain dry due to the higher rate of evaporation.

Professor Jettmar tried destroying fly maggots with chemicals in China in 1938. He came to the conclusion that the best method of killing larvae on a large scale was to use not chemicals but hot water. A large amount of boiling water suddenly poured over the surface of the latrine mass instantly kills all fly larvae (Jettmar 1940). The method was applied in boreholes but should certainly not be tried in compost latrines!

Chemical control

You can prevent fly breeding by keeping the receptacle filled with smoke. The method is best suited for large, specially designed latrines like the one illustrated in figure 146 (van Riel 1965).

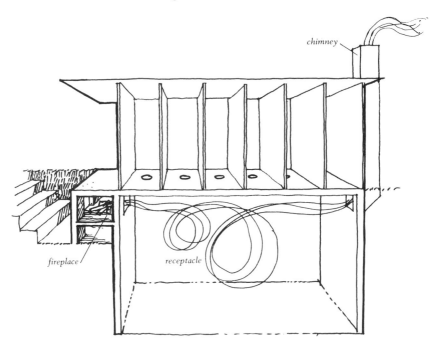

Figure 146   A multi-unit latrine with woodfire smoke for insect control

A variation of this method, at one time used for military latrines in East Africa, was to keep a smoking woodfire in a perforated kerosene tin suspended halfway down the pit by wires. It was necessary to renew the fire twice a day.

The introduction of DDT for insect control during World War II was initially successful. DDT was for example a major weapon in the control of fly-transmitted dysentery epidemics in Italy. Other organochloride insecticides such as Dieldrin were discovered and put to use soon afterwards. These compounds and their relatives had the advantage of having a persistent effect which usually lasted for months.

In many parts of the world, however, house flies and related species soon developed resistance to organochloride insecticides. Today insecticide resistance in these insects extends even to the new organophosphates, carbamates and pyrethroids. The enemies of the fly are also affected by the insecticide but are not able to develop resistance as fast as the fly. The end result of using insecticides against the house fly is therefore an increase in the fly population as well as a destruction of desirable organisms. Insecticides are toxic to man – when used persistently there is a risk that groundwater and soil will be polluted. An additional disadvantage of chemical insecticides is that they are too expensive for most fly-infested communities in developing countries. In short: insecticides cannot be relied upon for fly control in latrines.

The same is true for mosquito control. *Culex* mosquitoes are naturally tolerant to organochlorides, and resistance to organophosphates and carbamates is already widespread. Resistance to the newer pyrethroids is beginning to appear.

Synthetic insect growth regulators are showing promise against *Culex* but the high content of organic matter in latrines is a problem.

Experimental work on the use of synthetic hormones in preventing the growth of flies in manure has been carried out in the USA (Anon. 1975). The hormones, similar to some insect hormones, are incorporated in the feed of cattle and chickens and permeate the manure. When tested on four of the most important species of flies they proved 100% effective. The hormones have been derived from terpene chemicals with a relatively simple manufacturing process. There are no reports on what might happen to humans who consume the products of the cattle and chickens fed on hormones. If the hormones were also to permeate the human faeces this would open up a completely new prospect for fly control in latrines.

Biological control

In all latrines there is naturally a certain amount of biological control of the fly and mosquito population. The most obvious one is carried out by reptiles. Lizards and chameleons are great devourers of flies and a latrine and its immediate surroundings is one of their favourite locations. Lizards often live inside the receptacle. Spiders may be even more important and in many latrines the space between the pile and the squatting slab is filled with spider webs. Frogs can also easily survive in a compost latrine.

Less obvious but equally or more important is the biological control carried out by tiny fly parasites and pathogens. Several species can be released in the fly breeding area where they live on fly eggs, larvae and pupae. The most widely used are *Tachenandphagus zelandicus*, *Spalangia indus* and *Mucidifurax raptor* (Parker 1977).

T. zelandicus is native to New Zealand and Australia. It can lay 5–10 eggs in a single maggot. The immature stages of the life cycle last 22 days at 21°C and the adult lives 8 to 15 days.

S. indus is a hot-weather parasite native to California. It attacks the fly pupae, puncturing the outer pupal wall. Its immature life cycle is 22 days at 27°C and the adult lives 30 to 40 days. *M. raptor* is similar to *S. indus* in activity.

Neoaplectana nematodes can also be used for the control of insects. The nematodes attack larvae of the house fly, tse-tse flies, cockroaches, etc. (Dr A.E. Pye 1982, personal communication).

Agriculturalists have for many years known that several of the rod-shaped bacilli are insect pathogens. The bacilli concerned cause fatal disease in the larvae of certain insects, including the house fly and the mosquito.

Bacillus thuringiensis has proved effective against fly breeding in pit latrines and compost latrines in Tanzania (Carlberg *et al.* 1984) and in Mexico (J. Mena 1984, personal communication). *B. thuringiensis* H14 and *B. sphaericus* have shown good results in field trials against mosquitoes.

Conclusions

No one measure alone is likely to achieve complete fly control. For pit and compost latrines in developing countries action should be based on a combination of the following methods:

- A lid, preferably a self-closing flap-trap, should be included. All other openings to the receptacle must be screened and holes and cracks immediately repaired.
- The user should sprinkle ashes, lime, husks or powdered earth over each deposit of faeces.
- Lizards, frogs, spiders and *B. thuringiensis* should be encouraged to live and multiply in the receptacle.
- Compost latrines should, whenever possible, be constructed with a simple solar heat collector over the receptacle.

REFERENCES

Anonymous (1975) Killing flies with hormones, *Ceres*, 8(4), 67.

Asklund, L., Johansson, S., Kalnins-Nilsson, A. and Selander, K. (1972) *Ouargla – rapport från en algerisk ökenstad*, Thesis (Mimeo.), Dept of Architecture, University of Lund, Sweden.

Behringer, A. (1959) *Das Mauerbuch*, 9th edn, Otto Maier Verlag, Ravensburg, West Germany.

Bells Asbestos & Engineering Africa Ltd (undated) *ROEC sanitation – installation instructions,* Johannesburg, South Africa.

Bruce, M.E. (1967) *Commonsense compost making*, Faber & Faber, London, UK.

van Buren, A., McMichael, J.K., Caceres, A. and Caceres, R. (1984) Dry-composting latrines in Guatemala, *Ambio* (in press).

Carlberg, G., Kihamia, C. and Minjas, J. (1984) *Microbial control of flies in latrines in Dar es Salaam with a Bacillus thuringiensis preparation, MUSCABAC* (Mimeo.), Dept of Microbiology, University of Helsinki, Finland.

Carter, J.C. (1938) The bored-hole latrine, *Bull. Hyg.*, 13(8), 591–9.

Curtis, C.F. and Hawkins, P.M. (1982) Entomological studies of on-site sanitation systems in Botswana and Tanzania, *Trans. R. Soc. Trop. Med. Hyg.*, 76(1), 99–108.

Democratic Republic of Vietnam, Ministry of Health, Dept of Hygiene and Epidemiology (1968) *Double septic tanks* (Mimeo.), Hanoi, Vietnam.

Dorozynski, A. (1975) When is waste a waste?, *Ceres*, 8(5), 70.

FAO/SIDA (1975) *Organic materials as fertilizer*, Soils Bulletin No. 27, Rome, Italy.

Fogel, M. (1977) *Chemical analysis of Clivus Multrum compost* (Mimeo.), Clivus Multrum USA Inc., Cambridge, MA, USA.

Gibbs, K. (1984) Privacy and the pit privy – technology or technique?, *Waterlines*, 3(1), 19–21.

Gurak, R., Kilama, W. and Winblad, U. (1977) Compost latrines in Tanzania – a preliminary report, *Compost Sci.*, 18(4), 20–3.

Handa, B.K. (1975) *Rural latrine*, National Environmental Engineering Research Institute, Nagpur, India.

India, Central Public Health Engineering Research Institute (1964) Evaluation of rural latrine designs, *Proceedings of the Symposium*, Nagpur, India.

India, Institute of Social Science Trust (1981) *Rural sanitation — technology options*, Rural Technology Series, Delhi, India.

India, Technology Advisory Group (1982) *Manual on the design, construction and maintenance of low-cost pour-flush water seal latrines in India*, UNDP Project IND/81/014, Lucknow, India.

Jettmar, H.M. (1940) Some experiments on the resistance of the latrine fly, *Chrysomyia megacephala*, against chemicals, *Chinese Med. J.*, 57, 74–85.

Kern, K. (1970) *The owner-built home*, Specialty Printing Co., Yellow Springs, OH, USA.

Kirkman, J. (1976) *City of Sanaa*, World of Islam Publishing Co Ltd, London, UK.

Lewcock, R. (1976) Towns and buildings in Arabia – N. Yemen, *Arch. Ass. Quarterly* 8(1), 4–19.

McGarry, M. and Stainforth, J. (eds) (1978) *Compost fertilizer and biogas production from human and farm wastes in the People's Republic of China*, IDRC, Ottawa, Canada.

McMichael, J. K. (ed.) (1976) *Health in the third world — studies from Vietnam*, Spokesman Books, Nottingham, UK.

Morgan, P.R. and Mara, D.D. (1982) *Ventilated improved pit latrines: recent developments in Zimbabwe*, World Bank Technical Paper No. 3, The World Bank, Washington DC, USA.

van Nostrand, J. and Wilson, J.D. (1983) *The ventilated improved double-pit latrine: a construction manual for Botswana*, TAG Technical Note No. 3, The World Bank, Washington DC, USA.

Parker, J.L. (1977) Aggressive little parasites will dine on fly larvae, *Countryside*, 61(6), 40.

Patel, I. (1970) *Safai-marg darshika (A guide book on sanitation)*, Udyogshala Press, Delhi, India.

du Pradal, P. (1982) *Environmental sanitation and protection project: final evaluation*, USAID, Washington DC, USA.

Reiter, P. (1978) Expanded polystyrene balls: an idea for mosquito control. *Ann. Trop. Med. Parasitol.*, 72(6), 595–6.

van Riel, J. (1965) *Santé publique tropicale*, Éditions Desoer, Liège, Belgium.

Roy, A.K. (1981) *Planning and designing of large scale pour-flush latrine programme in urban areas*, UNCHS Ad Hoc Expert Group on Appropriate Infrastructure Services, Working Paper HS/Conf. 1/81/18, Nairobi, Kenya.

Ryan, B.A. and Mara, D.D. (1983) *Ventilated improved pit latrines: vent pipe design guidelines*, TAG Technical Note No. 6, The World Bank, Washington DC, USA.

Sale, C. (1929) *The specialist*, Specialist Publishing Co., Carmel, CA, USA.

Satrom, G. and Stephens, D. (1979) *A fly control handbook* (Mimeo), Beneficial Biosystems Inc., Emeryville, CA, USA.

United States, Treasury Dept, Public Health Service (1933) *The sanitary privy*, Supplement No. 108 to the Public Health Reports, Government Printing Office, Washington DC, USA.

West, L.S. (1951) *The housefly*, Comstock Publishing Co., Ithaca, NY, USA.

Wagner, E.G. and Lanoix, J.N. (1958) *Excreta disposal for rural areas and small communities*, WHO Monograph Series No. 39, Geneva, Switzerland.

GLOSSARY*

absorptive capacity
The ability of the pit walls to take up liquid matter
aerobes, aerobic
Micro-organisms which require air to maintain life
anaerobes, anaerobic
Micro-organisms which will not grow in the presence of air
anal cleaning
Removing faeces from around the anus (the opening in the body from where they are excreted)
antibiotic
Medicine that fights infections caused by bacteria [DW]
ascaris (roundworm)
Large worms that live in people's intestines
auger
Tool for boring holes in soil

bacteria
Small germs that cannot be seen with the naked eye
biogas
Gas containing mainly methane. Can be produced by anaerobic decomposition

C/N ratio
Ratio of weight percentage of organic carbon (C) and total nitrogen (N) in, for example, a compost
carrier
An apparently healthy person (or animal) who harbours a pathogen and passes it to the environment
chemotherapy
Use of a chemical agent to treat a disease

---

* Terms followed by [DW] are taken from Werner, D. (1980) *Where there is no doctor*, Macmillan, London and Basingstoke; those followed by [AG] are from Godman, A. (1972) *Health science for the tropics*, Longman, Singapore.

compost latrine

A drop latrine into which carbon-rich materials (kitchen leftovers, grass, straw, ash, sawdust) are added to the excreta. The end product of the composting process is humus

composting

A biological process in which various organisms under controlled conditions break down organic matter into humus

DDT

An insecticide

decomposition

A biological process in which various organisms break down organic matter

defecate

The way of passing faeces out of the body (to shit)

double-vault latrine

See 'vault'

drop latrines

Latrines where excreta fall through a hole or a chute into a receptacle

environment

The world of living and non-living things near any animal or plant which can affect it [AG]

excreta

Mixture of faeces and urine from human beings

faeces

Waste matter excreted from the bowel, consisting mainly of cellulose, un-absorbed food, intestinal secretions and micro-organisms (stools, shit)

final disposal

Getting rid of excreta in such a way that they cannot be used again

fissured rock

Rock containing many cracks

flukes

Worms that infect the liver or other parts of the body and cause different diseases. Blood flukes get into the blood and cause schistosomiasis [DW]

flush latrine

Latrine where excreta are flushed away with water

germ

Very small organisms that can grow in the body and cause some infectious diseases (micro-organisms) [DW]

groundwater

Water under the surface of the ground

humus

The end product of decomposition. A major ingredient in topsoil

hygiene

Actions or practices of personal cleanliness that lead to good health [DW]

impermeable

Water-tight

infection

A sickness caused by bacteria or other germs [DW]

insecticide

A poison that kills insects

larvae

The young worm-like form that comes from the egg of many insects and parasites [DW]

maggot

Larvae from flies

manure

Animal droppings (dung) and urine, and possibly also bedding

micro-organism

A tiny plant or animal so small it cannot be seen with the naked eye

Multrum

A type of compost latrine developed in Sweden

organisms

Living things (animals or plants) [DW]

organochlorides

Organic chemicals containing chlorides

parasites, parasitic

Worms and tiny animals that live in or on another animal or person and cause harm [DW]

pathogen

An organism which is capable of causing disease

permeable

Describes soils through which water can freely drain

pH

A measure of acidity/alkalinity. The scale runs from 0 to 14. A value of 7 stands for netrality, higher values indicate alkalinity and lower values acidity

pollute, pollution

Make water (air, soil) foul or filthy

prevention
Action taken to stop sickness before it starts [DW]
protozoa
The smallest type of animal life, e.g. amoeba

receptacle
A pit or a container where excreta are stored
residual product, residue
Material left over in process or consumption
retention time
The period of time excreta are kept in the receptacle

sanitation
Excreta disposal, and cleanliness in relation to excreta disposal
superstructure
Construction above ground (shelter)

taboo
Something that is avoided, banned or not allowed because of a cultural belief [DW]
toxic
Poisonous
transmit
To pass on, transfer, or allow to spread from one person to another [DW]

urine
Liquid waste from the body (piss, pee) [DW]

vault
An underground chamber. A latrine with a receptacle divided into two chambers (vaults) is called a double-vault latrine
vector
That which carries a disease, e.g. insects [AG]
virus
Germs smaller than bacteria [DW]

washer
A person using water for anal cleaning
waste
Discarded residue to be disposed of and for which reason it is considered of no value (human waste = excreta)
waste disposal
Final disposal of waste or its transformation into humus

water table
    The level where water is found when a hole is dug
wiper
    A person using some solid material (paper, rags, grass, sticks, stones) for anal cleaning

INDEX

159